MEZZOGIORNO SETTANTA

ISTITUTO GEOGRAFICO DE AGOSTINI - NOVARA

This publication documents some of the salient aspects of special intervention in Southern Italy and is intended to increase awareness of the effort being made by the nation to confront and to resolve the major, centuries-old problem of the South, still in the forefront of national economic and social policy matters.

The volume is confined to pictorial illustration of projects developed with financing provided by the *Cassa per il Mezzogiorno* (Southern Italy Development Agency): the choice of projects illustrated has been guided not only by criteria of the technical and financial commitment involved, but also of the accruing economic and social benefits. In this way it is possible visually to depict the new countenance of Southern Italy, to provide evidence of the process of environmental transformation and human advancement now under way in the South and of the determinant results attained so far, despite the manifold difficulties which the *Cassa per il Mezzogiorno,* as the principal instrument for implementation of policy for the South, has had to confront and overcome in the course of its operations.

Our objective is therefore to project an image, albeit symbolic and incomplete, of the progress achieved in Southern Italy after twenty years of special intervention designed to eradicate a situation of social stagnation and economic underdevelopment.

This in no way signifies that the problems of the South have been resolved: but the perspective of those problems has changed with the advancement of the people. From many viewpoints the new problems may be more complex than those originally encountered, but they can be approached in a situation which is objectively very different and more soundly based.

The visitor returning to the South after an absence of twenty years is immediately impressed by the intervening transformation. Entire valleys and plains, once marshy and malaria-ridden, or arid and barren, have been reclaimed and irrigated and are now the scene of flourishing agriculture and modernly equipped farms; thousands of villages and hamlets, formerly without water, are now supplied by the distribution systems that have been created; hundreds of kilometres of roads, driven through the erstwhile inviolate territory of the South, have freed hundreds of localities from their centuries-old isolation; development of industrial and tourist projects continues apace, stimulated by the provision of financial incentives and by other facilities contemplated by law.

But it is the social progress of the people of the South which most impresses the returning visitor: the increase of consumption in general, of the volume of car traffic, of the incidence of radio, television, telephones, the all-round improvement of living conditions – indisputable evidence of the qualitative advance achieved in these first twenty years of special intervention in Southern Italy.

The contents of this publication provide evidence of the moral and political commitment undertaken by the State towards the people of the South and at the same time confirm the substantial validity of the basic choices which, revised in the light of changed requirements, provide for global and organic intervention as the most suitable strategy for achieving the definitive liberation of Southern Italy from the demoralizing conditions of backwardness which have for so long prevailed: intervention that will enable the integration of the South into a modern evolutive process, thereby facilitating the elimination of the social and economic disequilibria that still persist in Italy.

Enzo Gambino

SICILY

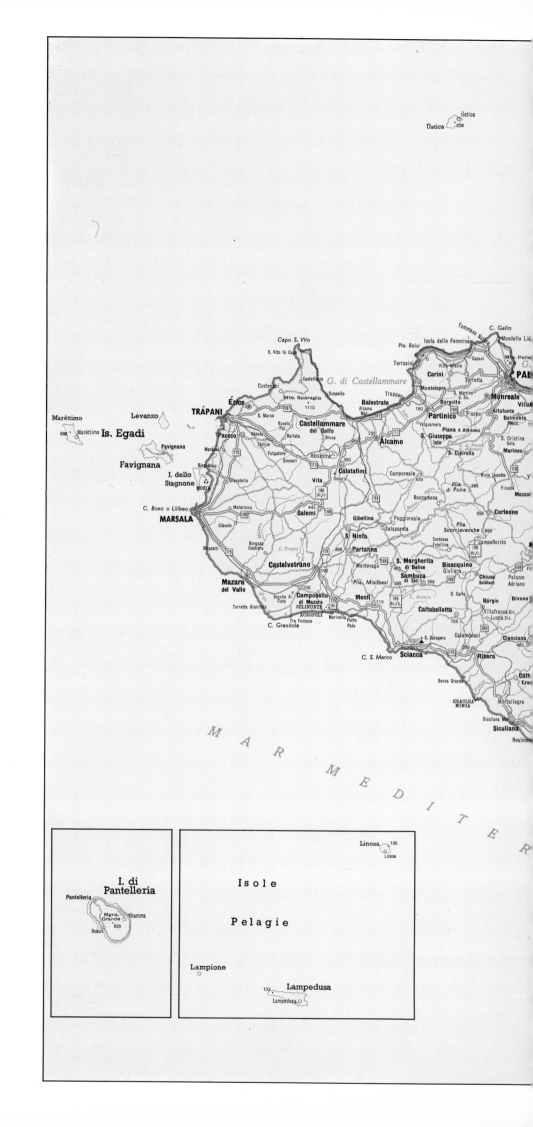

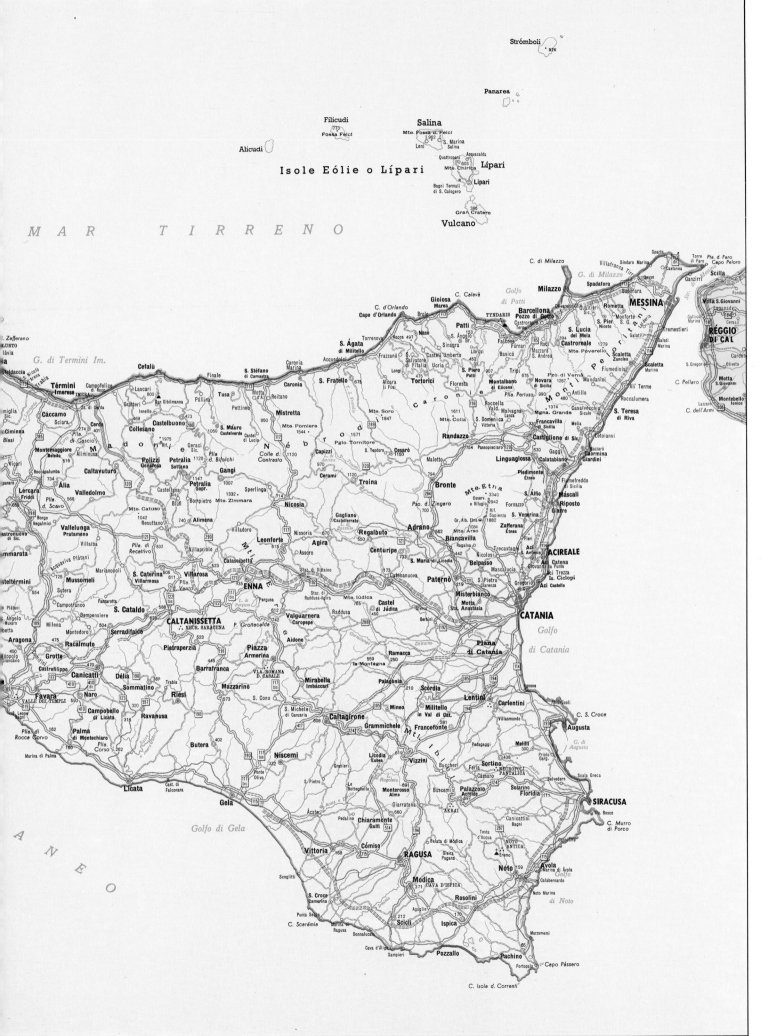

The Priolo-Melilli petrochemicals complex, seen at night. The plant occupies approximately 400 hectares in the Siracusa Industrial Development Area. New industrial projects established in Sicily to date have involved aggregate investment of over US $ 2,272 million.

1 — The 81-metre bridge which carries the Pettineo-Castel di Lucio (Messina) highway across the Tusa torrent.

2 — A section of the Catania coastal road, 24 metres wide and more than 2 kilometres long.

3 — A viaduct on the Porto Empedocle-Agrigento-S. Cataldo road. Twelve bridges and viaducts, for a total length of approximately 2 kilometres, and a 412-metre tunnel are included among the structures required for completion of this 57-kilometre road. Shorter by 22 kilometres than the former national highway, the new road handles the particularly heavy traffic deriving from the considerable industrial and tourist development of the Porto Empedocle, Agrigento and Caltanissetta areas and from the Racamulto and Castelfranco mines.

4 — Sharp bends on the tourist road leading up to Monte Pellegrino, which dominates the panorama of the city of Palermo. The 8-kilometre road links Mondello with the S. Rosalia Sanctuary.

5 — A viaduct on the Gela-Caltagirone-Catania highway. The Cassa built 58 kilometres of this 91-kilometre artery which, together with the Porto Empedocle-Agrigento-Caltanissetta and Ragusa-Catania highways, forms an organic system that has practically resolved the road-traffic problem in south-eastern Sicily.

6 — The S. Michele viaduct on the Palermo-Punta Raisi highway. Apart from linking Palermo with the airport, this 17-kilometre double-carriageway artery also meets the requirements of an area in which the volume of traffic is steadily increasing.

4

5

6

1 — A 150-metre pipeline-bridge of the Alcantara (Messina) water-supply system. The bridge is one of the many structures forming part of this major 65-kilometre system which, with a flow-rate of 595 litres per second, supplies the 350,000 population of Messina and of 17 other municipalities in the Province. The island's water-supply system comprises more than 1,160 kilometres of pipeline and supplies 144 localities with an aggregate population of 1,365,000.

2 — A detail of the huge tanks of the plant, capable of treating 130,000 cubic metres of water per day, which supplements the domestic supply of the city of Palermo.

3 — The building which houses plant for the intake, through a 700-metre tunnel, of water from the Gurno, Cottanera and S. Bartolomeo springs, which is then distributed by the Alcantara water-supply system. In all, 209 adduction works have been completed in Sicily, enabling the utilization of approximately 3,530 litres of water per second.

4 — The Agghiastro whirlpool basin, which regulates pipeline pressures, is another important facility for the water-supply of Palermo.

5 — The Scanzano earth-fill dam on the river Eleuterio (Palermo) is 45 metres high and 400 metres long. The storage capacity of the reservoir is 17 million cubic metres of water which, with a flow-rate of 1,500 litres per second, feeds Palermo's auxiliary water-supply system. Some 178 reservoirs, for an aggregate capacity of over 140,000 cubic metres, have been built in Sicily for the supply of domestic water to the island's population.

3

4

5

1 — A weir across the Belice, one of a series of works carried out to control the flow of the river in order to avoid flooding of the surrounding land. Similar water-course control works for a total volume of 1½ million cubic metres have been completed in Sicily.

2 — Panorama of a citrus-fruit farm in the locality of Pantano di Lentini (Catania). Land-transformation programmes financed in Sicily have enabled the construction of 8,500 farmhouses, 1,000 kilometres of inter-farm roads and water-supply systems for 195 rural localities.

3 — A wine-making co-operative at Castelvetrano (Trapani), capable of processing 135,000 quintals of grapes for an annual production of 105,000 hectolitres of wine. A further 76 wine-making plants, with a total productive capacity of more than 1.1 million hectolitres, have been financed in Sicily.

4 — Interior of one of the 6,000 cattle sheds built in the island with Cassa financing, providing accommodation of approximately 40,000 head of cattle.

5 — Panorama of the Pozzillo dam on the Salso (Enna), built in concrete blocks. The dam is 59 metres high, 403 metres long and enables storage of 141 million cubic metres of water, which is used for irrigation of the Plain of Catania and for hydroelectric production. In all, 7 dams have so far been built in the island, providing an aggregate storage capacity of approximately 360 million cubic metres of water, utilized for domestic supply, irrigation, power production and industrial processes.

6 — The earth-fill Trinità dam on the river Delia (Trapani), seen at night. The reservoir formed by the 25-metre high, 320-metre long dam, has a storage capacity of 18.1 million cubic metres of water, utilized for the irrigation of over 4,000 hectares of land in the areas of Mazara del Vallo and Castelvetrano.

3

4

5

6

1 — The Poma earth-fill dam on the river Iato (Palermo) is 49 metres high, 237 metres long and enables the storage of 64.5 million cubic metres of water, utilized for the irrigation of land between Castellammare del Golfo and Partinico.

2 — One of the irrigation channels on the left bank of the river Simeto. The irrigation distribution system in Sicily exceeds 2,000 kilometres in length and supplies a total area of approximately 55,000 hectares.

3 — Panorama of the siphon and penstock fed by the Pozzillo and Ancipa reservoirs. The reinforced steel pipes are 2.2 metres in diameter and convey the water to the Ponte Barca hydroelectric power station. The water is subsequently utilized to supply the extensive system for the irrigation of 33,100 hectares in the Plain of Catania and of approximately 3,000 hectares in the Plain of Lentini.

1 — A secondary canal in the Plain of Catania, where the irrigation system is 1,310 kilometres long. Prior to special intervention only 3,200 hectares of this plainland were irrigated: completion of the works on hand will enable irrigation of some 43,000 hectares.

2 — An orange grove in the area of Paternò (Catania), a typical example of the results of organic agricultural transformation. In the Plain of Catania alone 2.8 million quintals of citrus fruit are grown each year.

3 — Interior of a greenhouse for growing vegetables in the Scicli locality (Ragusa). This land reclamation district is supplied predominantly from the river Irminio and by the numerous wells excavated along the entire coastal strip.

4 — Panorama of another greenhouse complex, in the Plain of Gela. In this area the irrigation system supplies approximately 5,200 hectares of land and a further 1,500 hectares will be irrigable upon completion of work at present on hand. In Sicily 40 greenhouse complexes, covering an aggregate of approximately 33,500 square metres, have been built to date with financing provided under the terms of special intervention.

5 — Irrigation plant in the valley of the Belice-Carboi. The entire system of the area is supplied by water from the Arancio reservoir, on the Carboi, with a storage capacity of 33 million cubic metres taken-off from the river Belice, providing a flow rate of 600 litres per second for an irrigable area totalling approximately 6,600 hectares.

3

4

5

1 — Detail of the oil refinery at Augusta (Siracusa).

2 — Adduction canal for the supply of water for industrial utilization in the Gela petrochemicals complex (Caltanissetta).

3 — Panorama of the oil refinery at Milazzo (Messina).

4 — A stage in the production of steel valves at Patti (Messina).

5 — The Gagliano natural-gas storage and processing facility at Enna. The deposits of natural gas discovered in Sicily are destined to make a valuable contribution to the island's industrial development.

1

3

4

5

1 — Aerial view of part of the Catania Industrial Development Area, where already many manufacturing and processing plants have been established. Major road, rail and water-supply works have been completed or are on hand to provide the area with efficient infrastructures.

2 — Wine-making factory at Casteldaccia (Palermo).

3 — Department of a mens clothing factory at Enna.

4 — Detail of a building of the large plant at Villafranca Tirrena (Messina) for the production of tyres and light motorcycles.

5 — Plant and equipment of a Messina brewery.

6 — Offshore view of a petrochemicals plant in the locality of Siracusa. To date some 40 plants, mainly in the petrochemicals and engineering sectors, have been established in the 1,800-hectare Siracusa Industrial Development Area, for which a series of major infrastructures have been created.

3

4

5

6

1 — Panorama of the north-eastern coast of Sicily, seen from a hotel at Taormina (Messina). The ancient traditions of this major Sicilian coastal resort continue to attract large numbers of Italian and foreign tourists. Throughout Sicily financing has been provided for the construction of 122 new hotels, enabling accommodation for a further approximately 13,000 visitors.

2 — The Temple of Selinunte (Trapani). Known as « E » (or Herajon), the Temple is one of the most famous Doric monuments recalling Greek civilization in the island, and was brought to light after patient and expert excavation.

3 — The colourful mosaics discovered in the remains of the Roman villa at Casale di Piazza Armerina (Enna). By virtue of their size and beauty the mosaics represent a truly unique archaeological treasure, now on view for the admiration of visitors thanks to demanding restoration work and scrupulous conservation.

4 — The Etna cableway (Catania), which links the Sapienza station with the Volcanological Observatory located in an area of great attraction to tourists and winter-sports enthusiasts. The cablecars complete the 4,200-metre journey in only 18 minutes.

5 — The Grecian Theatre at Taormina (Messina) dominates an area of particularly beautiful natural scenery. Originally built during the Greek civilization of around the III century B.C., the theatre was subsequently enlarged by the Romans. Despite the fact that many of the structures had been removed, under the aegis of the Cassa the theatre was restored to its ancient splendour, fittingly preserved and valorized. Throughout Sicily 73 projects have been completed for the renovation, excavation and restoration of works of particular archaeological, artistic and monumental importance.

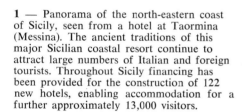

3

4

5

1 — The terrace and building of the Pace del Mela (Messina) nursery-school, with accommodation for 60 children. A total of 74 nursery schools have been built in Sicily with special intervention financing.

2 — The 300-bed hospital at Modica (Ragusa) is one of the five new hospitals built in Sicily.

3 — The new hospital building at Milazzo, with 350 beds.

4 — Caltagirone (Catania) hospital, enlarged and completed by the Cassa, has 460 beds. The hospitals programme for Sicily has enabled, apart from new construction, the expansion and modernization of 7 hospitals, increasing the aggregate availability of beds by 3,200.

3

4

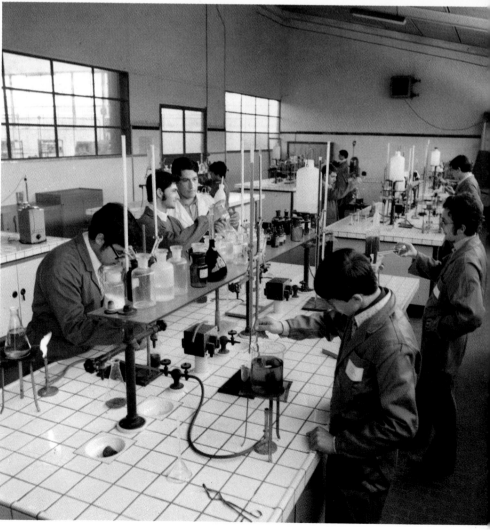

1 — Special intervention has considerably assisted and encouraged the island's traditional handicraft activities, typical of which is pottery.

2 — The chemistry laboratories of the Inter-company Industrial Vocational Training Centre (CIAPI) at Priolo (Siracusa). Built in 1964, the Centre trains 1,000 students each year for the chemicals, electrical, electronics, engineering and hot-working sectors.

3 — The entrance to the Agricultural Vocational Training Institute at Lentini (Siracusa). Built in 1962, the Institute specializes young people for employment in citrus-fruit cultivation.

4 — ISIDA at Palermo, which houses the Institute for the advanced training of industrial management personnel.

5 — An experimental greenhouse at the Agricultural Training Institute, Giarre (Catania). Created in 1962, the Institute trains young people in modern techniques employed in the various sectors of agriculture.

6 — Fishing boats moored at Mazara del Vallo (Trapani), one of the principal fishing centres in Southern Italy. Cassa intervention has enabled the strengthening of the fishing fleet in the South with approximately 5,800 new craft and the building of 35 deep-sea fishing vessels.

3

4

5

6

1 — A view of Pantelleria, showing typical terraced cultivation. Special intervention projects include completion of the coastal road circling the island and construction of a reservoir for the accumulation of 2,000 cubic metres of domestic water. Currently under construction is a desalination plant capable of processing 1,000 cubic metres of water per day. These projects will assist the tourist development of the island, where accommodation facilities have already been increased with the construction of modern hotels providing 300 further beds.

2 — A view of the coast of Lipari, one of the Aeolian group of islands, showing the white pumice caves, which provide added interest to visitors to the island, whose economy is based principally on tourism. Special intervention has been directed predominantly at valorization of the natural beauty of all the smaller Sicilian islands, through the construction of hotels and holiday villages, which have to date provided an increase of 700 beds in the Aeolian islands alone. On Lipari a loop road has been built linking the localities of Canneto, Acquacalda, Quattropani and Pianoconte with the town of Lipari. Archeological excavation in the vicinity of Filicudi has revealed the existence of a flourishing pre-Greek civilization in the archipelago. The precious discoveries are now exhibited in a specially built museum.

3 — A beach on Stromboli, another of the Aeolian islands. Also on Stromboli intervention has been directed at improving roads and water supply and at stimulating tourism. The crater of the volcano can now be reached rapidly from the port of S. Bartolomeo.

4-5 — Lampedusa, Linosa and Lampione form the Pelagian group. In view of the complete absence of local resources, water supply of all the small islands presented a serious problem. The solution was approached by building large-capacity reservoirs for filling from tankers and by developing supply systems ensuring efficient distribution. On Lampedusa, the larger of the two islands, construction is nearing completion of a desalination plant capable of processing 500 cubic metres of water per day.

6 — Part of the Aeolian archipelago seen from the island of Vulcano.

7 — A section of the Leni-Rinella road, on the island of Salina, forming part of a more extensive network built to link the coastal villages, formerly accessible only by sea.

8 — The picturesque harbour of Ustica. Also on this island works for improving water-supply have been carried out, and special intervention in the hotel sector has assisted in the provision of a further 100 beds.

4

5

6

7

8

SARDINIA

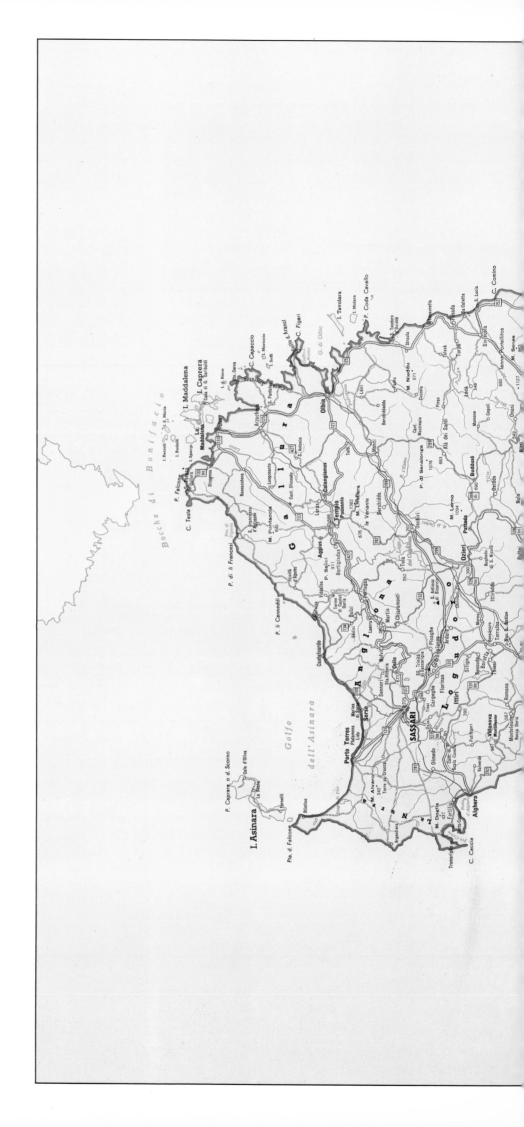

M A R

T I R R E N O

D I

S A R D E G N A

M E D I T E R R A N E O

G. di Orosei

Golfo di Cagliari

G. di Oristano

G. d'Asinara

G. di Palmas

NUORO

CAGLIARI

Oristano

Bosa

Dorgali

Tortolì

Dolianova

Sinnai

Quartu S. Elena

Iglesias

Carbonia

Carloforte

S. Antioco

I. di S. Pietro

I. di S. Antioco

Campidano

Barbagia

Sarrabus

Gerrei

Sulcis

C. Marargiu · C. Mannu · C. S. Marco · C. Frasca · C. Pecore · C. Teulada · C. Sperone · C. di Pula · C. Spartivento · C. Carbonara · C. Ferrato · C. S. Lorenzo · C. di M. Santu

Concrete dam across the Mulargia (Cagliari). The reservoir formed by the 99-metre high, 272-metre long dam has a storage capacity of 334 million cubic metres and, together with the Nuraghe Arrubiu reservoir on the Flumendosa, provides water for the irrigation of 100,000 hectares in the area of Campidano di Cagliari and for the production of electricity. In Sardinia nine dams have been built so far, providing an aggregate storage capacity of approximately 800 million cubic metres of water.

1 - Viaduct across the Punta Gennarta (Cagliari) reservoir. The road replaces the section of the Iglesias highway submerged when the artificial lake was created.

2 — The « Tyrsus » ferry boat, one of three identical vessels operated between Sardinia and the mainland. The 5,000-ton ships have a cruising speed of 17/19 knots and can each carry 350 passengers, 74 automobiles and 30 rail freight-cars or 45 lorries.

3 — The Golfo Aranci-Olbia (Sassari) branch line, one of the auxiliary facilities of the ferry service. The 20-kilometre loop links the Golfo Aranci landing-stage with the island's rail system.

4 — A 175-metre viaduct across the river Tirso. This is one of the major structures on the 56-kilometre Abbasanta-Nuoro highway which provides communication with important areas of central Sardinia, formerly isolated, and links them with the port of Olbia.

5 — The Bardosu-Ottana (Nuoro) road now enables fast and easy travel between Ottana and National Highway 129. Construction of the 11-kilometre road presented a number of challenging problems, one of which was resolved with a 102-metre five-span bridge over the river Tirso.

6 — The bridge over the Carana (Sassari) is 63 metres long, the single central arch spanning a distance of more than 30 metres. The bridge is the major structure of the 12-kilometre road linking Luras with National Highway 133, from Tempio to Palau.

4

5

6

1 — The concrete Macheronis dam across the Posada (Nuoro) is 55.5 metres high and 340 metres long, providing a storage capacity of 28 million cubic metres of water for the irrigation of 4,300 hectares of land in the plains of Siniscola, Posada and Torpé.

2 — The concrete Punta Gennarta dam across the Rio Canonica (Cagliari) is 59.5 metres high, 210 metres long and enables the storage of 12.7 million cubic metres of water, utilized for the irrigation of 4,000 hectares in the Cixerri valley.

3 — The concrete Nuraghe Arrubiu dam on the Flumendosa (Cagliari), 119 metres high and 315 metres long. The reservoir, with a storage capacity of 317 million cubic metres of water, forms part of the Flumendosa-Mulargia system.

4 — The concrete Goceano (Sassari) dam, 47.5 metres high and 341.7 metres long, creates a reservoir with a storage capacity of 3.5 million cubic metres of water for the domestic supply of 32 localities, with an aggregate population of 152,000, in the Provinces of Sassari and Nuoro.

5 — The Pedra e Othoni rock-fill dam across the Cedrino (Nuoro) has a sheet-steel mantle. The storage capacity of the reservoir formed by the 76.5-metre high, 228.7-metre long dam is 108.3 million cubic metres of water, partly utilized for the irrigation of 3,000 hectares of land in the areas of Galtellì and Orosei.

3

4

5

1 — The Villagrande Strisaili (Nuoro) treatment plant is fed by the Ogliastra aqueduct and provides 3,500 cubic metres of domestic water per day. The 72 kilometres of pipeline distribute water at the rate of 40 litres per second to 14 localities with a total population of 50,000 in the Province of Nuoro.

2 — Detail of the Nuoro treatment plant which processes for domestic utilization 10,600 cubic metres of water per day drawn from the Govossai aqueduct. The town of Nuoro and 15 provincial localities, for a total population of 100.000, are supplied through a distribution system of 122 kilometres of pipeline at a flow-rate of 123 litres per second.

3 — Intake traverse at Olbia (Sassari). The system supplies water at the rate of 41 litres per second to Olbia and surrounding localities, with a total population of 20,000. To date 93 intake works have been completed in Sardinia, providing an aggregate flow-rate of 412 litres per second.

4 — Spillway of the dam across the Govossai (Nuoro). The plant regulates the flow of water during periods of spate of the rivers that feed the reservoir, which has a storage capacity of approximately 3 million cubic metres.

5 — A tank of the Olbia (Sassari) treatment plant, which is capable of providing 3,540 cubic metres per day for domestic utilization.

3

4

5

1 — The Arborea (Cagliari) reservoir, with
a capacity of 350 cubic metres, is fed by the
Bau Pirastu water supply system, which
supplies a population of 67,000 in 16
provincial localities through a network of
134 kilometres of pipeline.

2 — Buddusò (Sassari) treatment plant, fed
by the Goceano aqueduct, provides 14,200
cubic metres of domestic water per day.
The system distributes water at the rate of
163.6 litres per second through 250
kilometres of pipeline to a population of
152,000 in 32 localities of the Provinces of
Sassari and Nuoro.

3 — Microfilters of the Bidighinzu (Sassari)
water-treatment plant, which provides 42,600
cubic metres per day for the supply of
Sassari and 31 provincial localities for a
total population of 290,000.

4 — Panorama of the Bidighinzu (Sassari).
dam and of the water-treatment plant. The
concrete dam is 34 metres high, 266.54 metres
long, and enables storage of 11 million
cubic metres of water for supply, with a
flow-rate of 493 litres per second, of the
232-kilometre long Bidighinzu water-supply
system. In Sardinia a total of 1,600 kilometres
of pipeline have been laid for the supply of
144 localities with an aggregate population
of more than 700,000.

5 — Plant of the Sassari reservoir, which
has a storage capacity of 6,000 cubic metres,
supplied by the Bidighinzu complex. The
reservoir is one of the 282 which have been
built in the island.

6 — The Nuraghi (Cagliari) reservoir has a
storage capacity of 130 cubic metres and is
fed by the Cabras water-supply system, which
supplies a population of 19,600 in 7 localities
in the Province of Cagliari through a network
of 235 kilometres of pipeline.

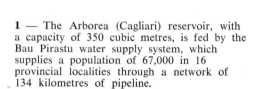

4

5

6

1 — The impressive steel bridge over the Coghinas (Sassari) supports a 62-metre long steel pipe through which water flows at the rate of 440 litres per second. The structure forms part of the system for distribution of water from the Castel Doria reservoir for the irrigation of approximately 2,000 hectares of land in the lower valley of the Coghinas. In Sardinia as a whole the 2,250-kilometre irrigation water distribution system supplies an area totalling approximately 260,000 hectares.

2 — The village of Villarios (Cagliari), created through land-improvement interventions, consists of more than 140 dwellings and of buildings for the provision of community services. More than 10,200 farmhouses have been built throughout Sardinia.

3 — Canal for the adduction of water from the reservoir on the river Posada (Nuoro). Water flows along the 4-kilometre canal at the rate of 3,476 litres per second into a distribution network for the irrigation of extensive areas of the Nuoro district.

4 — Three-way distribution plant in the valley of the river Coghinas (Sassari), one of the many installations of the 132-kilometre system for the irrigation of land situated to the left of the river.

5 — Detail of the collection centre of the milk station at Alghero (Sassari), which processes 36,000 quintals of milk per year. Fifteen new dairy farms have been established in Sardinia.

6 — Interior of a modern greenhouse established by a Consortium in southern Sardinia. The Consortium grows early vegetables and flowers for the Italian and foreign markets. In Sardinia 129 such projects have been developed.

1

3

4

5

6

1 — Aerial view of the Porto Torres (Sassari) petrochemicals plant. To date industrial projects have been promoted in Sardinia for an aggregate investment of approximately US $ 2,128 million.

2 — Berthing facilities for the Porto Torres petrochemicals plant, enabling the handling of ships of up to 100,000 tons laden weight.

3 — Detail of the synthetic fibres plant at Villacidro (Cagliari).

4 — Paper mills at Arbatax (Nuoro).

5 — A section of the oil refinery at Sarroch (Cagliari).

1

3

4

5

1 — Hydroelectric power plant fed by water from the Castel Doria (Sassari) reservoir.

2 — Interior of S. Miali (Cagliari) power station, one of the two underground plants which utilize the water of the Flumendosa-Mulargia system and which produce approximately 100 million kWh per year.

3 — Sulcis thermal power station at Portovesme (Cagliari) generates an average of 2,500 million kWh per annum.

4 — Taloro (Nuoro) hydroelectric plant, which has an annual average producibility of 150 million kWh, utilizes the water of the Gusana reservoir (storage capacity 58 million cubic metres).

3

4

1 — Panorama of the Cala Bitta tourist centre on the Costa Smeralda (Sassari). Provision of incentives for hotel development in Sardinia has led to an increase of more than 9,000 beds.

2-3 — The ancient Grottoes of Nettuno at the foot of the Capo Caccia (Sassari) precipice are among the most renowned of marine grottoes. Cassa intervention has made them accessible both by land, with the provision of perfectly landscaped steps and paths, and by sea, with the construction of a landing stage. Valorization of the grottoes has been completed with the opening of new internal passageways and with the illumination plant.

4 — The Santu Antine tower at Torralba (Sassari). Together with the Su Nuraxi tower, it represents one of the most important testimonies of the megalithic civilization in Sardinia. Built towards the end of the 9th century B.C., the tower, which dominates the Campu Giavesu depression, has been completely restored and consolidated. A further eighteen works of archaeological, historical and artistic importance in the island have been restored through Cassa intervention.

5 — Terrace of a 108-room hotel at Stintino (Sassari), providing 200 beds.

6 — A hotel on the Arzachena coast. In recent years 18 hotels, for a total of 3,650 beds, have been built on the Costa Smeralda, an area of particular tourist attraction.

2

4

1

5

6

1 — The 600-bed SS. Annunziata hospital at Sassari, completed in 1968, is equipped with the latest facilities.

2 — The nursing training school at Sassari Hospital.

3 — The Lanusei (Nuoro) nursery-school, which accommodates 90 children, is one of the hundred such schools built in Sardinia.

4 — The Bitti Garofai (Nuoro) nursery-school accommodates 90 children.

5 — The 230-bed hospital at Alghero (Sassari) was opened in 1968. Special intervention has enabled an increase of 2,060 in the number of hospital beds available in Sardinia.

3

4

5

1 — Interior of the workshops of the Cagliari Inter-company Vocational Training Centre, created in 1965 for the training of 600 students each year for employment in the electrical, engineering and hot-working sectors.

2 — The Muravera Agricultural Institute (Cagliari) has been training farming experts since 1958.

3 — Recreational facilities form part of residential schools, such as the Cagliari Industrial Training Centre, created in 1956 and accommodating 255 students each year for specialization in engineering and electrical technology.

4 — Buildings and equipment of the S. Maria La Palma Agricultural Training School, where young people are trained in flower-growing and dairy-farming.

5 — Experimental field of the Siniscola Agricultural Training Institute (Nuoro), created in 1960 for the specialization of agricultural, horticultural and floricultural experts.

1

3

4

5

CALABRIA

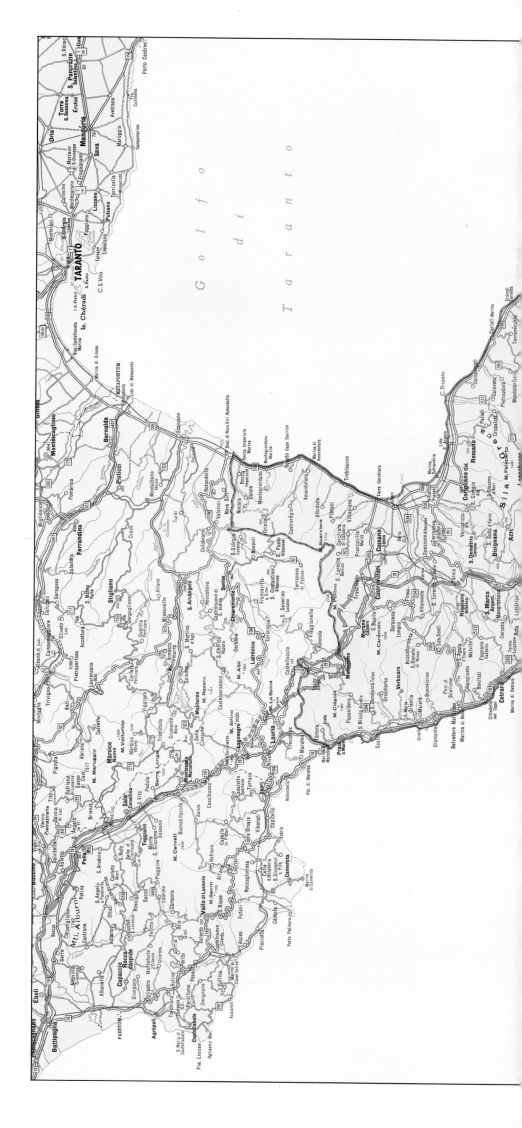

MAR TIRRENO

MARE IONIO

LA SILA

Sila Piccola

Golfo di Squillace

Golfo di S. Eufemia

Golfo di Gioia

ASPROMONTE

Isole Eólie o Lípari

Salina — Lípari — Vulcano — Panarea — Strómboli

Gran Cratere

Mte. Etna

Catanzaro
Cosenza
Crotone
Cutro
Nicastro
Sambiase
Rende
S. Lúcido
Amantea
Rogliano
S. Giovanni in Fiore
Serrastretta
Pizzo
Vibo Valentia
Tropea
Nicotera
Rosarno
Mileto
Gióia Táuro
Palmi
Bagnara Cal.
Scilla
Réggio di Cal.
Pellaro
Taurianova
Cittanova
Oppido Mamert.
Polistena
Cinquefrondi
Mámmola
Siderno
Locri
Caulónia
Roccella Iónica
Gerace
Bova
Bovalino Marina
Melissa
Scandale
S. Severina
Mesoraca
Sersale
Soverato
Chiaravalle Centrale
Serra S. Bruno

MESSINA
Milazzo
Barcellona Pozzo di Gotto
Patti
Tíndari
Castroreale
S. Lucia del Mela
Novara
Montalbano di Elicona
Castiglione di Sic.
Francavilla di Sic.
Linguaglossa
Randazzo
Bronte
Adrano
Biancavilla
Giarre
Riposto
Mascali
Fiumefreddo di Sicilia
Giardini
Taormina
S. Teresa di Riva
Letojanni
Scaletta
Gioiosa Marina
Tortorici
C. d'Orlando

The impressive structures of the viaduct
towering 112 metres above the Fiumarella,
on the artery linking Catanzaro with the
Due Mari highway. The arch spans a distance
of 231 metres of the total length of 467
metres of the 14-metre wide bridge, one of the
major works of its kind in Europe, the
construction of which required considerable
technical and financial effort.

1 — The initial section of the Due Mari highway, dominated by the bridge over the Fiumarella. The 40-kilometre highway provides easy communication between the Gulf of S. Eufemia on the Tyrrhenian coast to Squillace on the Ionian coast and replaces the former sections of the national highway which linked Catanzaro with the nearest railway station at S. Eufemia Lamezia along a winding 75-kilometre road.

2 — Double-tracking and electrification of the Battipaglia-Reggio Calabria line. Special intervention has helped to eliminate one of the most serious bottlenecks of the rail system in the South. The difficult geological nature of the terrain required the building of complex structures at certain points along the line.

3 — The 30-kilometre Rossano-Giamberga road facilitates communication between a number of important towns in the Province of Cosenza and the Sila highlands.

4 — The Ioppolo-Panaia road passes through numerous towns and villages in the Province of Catanzaro, providing continuity of the tourist route from the Tyrrhenian coast to Monte Poro.

5 — The coast road at Siderno (Reggio Calabria), 2 kilometres long and 16 metres wide, is linked to the Ionian national highway by two transversal branch-roads, thus enhancing the attraction of this important Calabrian tourist centre.

6 — The Reggio Calabria by-pass provides a fast, direct link between the terminal of the Autostrada del Sole and the new section of the Ionian national highway, thereby facilitating communication between the city and its industrial estate. The major structures along the by-pass are a 370-metre tunnel and 8 viaducts for a total length of 1,280 metres.

7 — Road in the Piani della Milea (Reggio Calabria) land-reclamation district. Built along the ridge of the Aspromonte, this 17-kilometre road eliminates the previous isolation of many villages by linking them with National Highways 111 and 112.

3

4

5

6

7

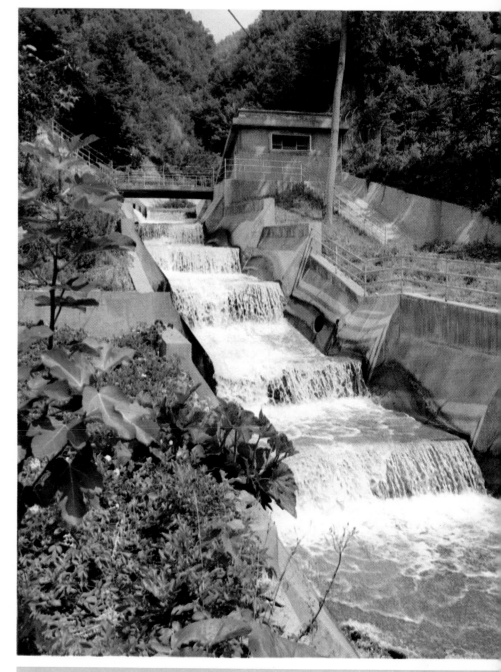

1 — Detail of the Ferrera water-supply system, which serves 21 towns and villages (including Paola, Amantea and S. Lucido), with a total population of 75,000, in the Provinces of Catanzaro and Cosenza. The system distributes water at a flow-rate of 84 litres per second through a 69-kilometre network of pipeline. In Calabria 448 intake works have been constructed, providing an aggregate flow rate of 4,350 litres of water per second.

2 — The Bianco tower-reservoir, with a storage capacity of 600 cubic metres, is supplied by the Bosco Bovalino water-supply system, which distributes water at a flow-rate of 40 litres per second to a number of municipalities and villages in the Province of Reggio Calabria, with a total population of 9,500. To date 506 reservoirs, for an aggregate storage capacity of 242,000 cubic metres, have been built in Calabria, for the water-supply of 323 localities with a total population of approximately 1.1 million.

3 — Detail of the plant of the reservoir which supplies the 1,300 population of Vena Superiore (Catanzaro) with water at the rate of 3 litres per second. The reservoir, with a storage capacity of 100 cubic metres, forms part of the Poro system for Vibo and Uniti, which distributes water at the rate of 90 litres per second through 46 kilometres of pipeline to 14 localities in the Province of Catanzaro with a population totalling over 30,000.

4 — A 600-cubic metre reservoir of the Caulonia Superiore water-supply system which, fed by wells in the bed of the Amusa torrent, distributes 12.5 litres of water per second to the 5,000 population of the Caulonia Superiore municipality in the Province of Reggio Calabria.

5 — Pre-stressed concrete girder carrying pipeline across the Novito torrent. The Novito system, fed by numerous springs, distributes water at the rate of 76 litres per second to 10 localities in the Province of Reggio Calabria, including Siderno, Locri and Ardore, with a total population of 69,000. At various points along the 43-kilometre pipeline system it was necessary to build complex structures across torrents. In Calabria as a whole the water-supply system comprises 2,352 kilometres of pipeline.

3

4

5

1 — This weir on the river Metramo forms part of the system fed by the river for the irrigation of 3,500 hectares of land in the Plain of Rosarno (Reggio Calabria). To date five similar intake works have been built in Calabria.

2 — Canal bridge, 90 centimetres in diameter, which adducts 700 litres of water per second from the La Verde torrent. It is one of the major works of the 95-kilometre La Verde irrigation system, which serves 1,080 hectares of land.

3 — Detail of the levees along the Allaro in the area of Caulonia (Reggio Calabria). Some 10 kilometres of the water course have been similarly consolidated in order to protect approximately 800 hectares of land from flooding. Because of the particular morphological conditions in Calabria, soil-protection measures are of considerable importance. In all, more than 600 kilometres of water-course control works have been completed, enabling the protection and drainage of approximately 60,000 hectares of land.

4 — The pumping plant on the river Petrace, which supplies water at the rate of 1,000 litres per second for distribution through a 100-kilometre network for the irrigation of 1,500 hectares of land in the Plain of Rosarno.

5 — Panorama of the Plain of Rosarno. Covering an area of 19,000 hectares, this district provides a typical example of the radical transformation achieved by means of special intervention. The Cassa has built five autonomous plants in the area, for the supply of a 600-kilometre irrigation distribution network. In the water-catchment areas of the surrounding mountains reafforestation, land consolidation and water-course control works have been carried out, whilst numerous roads have been built between the land-reclamation district and the major highways.

6 — Pumping plant on the Budello torrent in the Plain of Rosarno. The plant feeds a 53-kilometre distribution network for the irrigation of 920 hectares in the Gioia Tauro area.

7 — Flood-protection works close to Caulonia Superiore. Similar works have been completed for the protection of 262 villages in Calabria, whilst 11 communities have been transferred to localities less exposed to the hydro-geological hazards frequently encountered in many areas of the Region.

5

6

7

1 — A weir on the river Neto, from which water is drawn to supply a 345-kilometre distribution network for the irrigation of 6,500 hectares in the Plain of Crotone (Catanzaro). Some of the water is also channelled for utilization in the Crotone Industrialization Nucleus.

2 — A canal of the 130-kilometre distribution network for the irrigation of 4,400 hectares in the Plain of S. Eufemia. The system is supplied from a reservoir on the river Angitola.

3 — Panorama of the Plain of S. Eufemia. Also in this area considerable agricultural transformation is in progress, based on the cultivation of citrus fruit, olives and, more recently, strawberries. Besides intervention in the irrigation sector, financing provided by the Cassa and by the special legislation relating to Calabria has enabled the solution of many problems associated with drainage in this land-reclamation district, as well as the construction of a road network to facilitate the transportation and marketing of agricultural products.

4 — The primary dam of the Monte Marello reservoir on the Angitola (Catanzaro) is earth-built, with the up-stream wall lined with concrete slabs. Approximately 30 metres high and 147 metres long, the dam is the most important structure of its kind in Calabria. Other dams have been built at Tarsia on the Crati and at Votturino on the Ceraso. Aggregate storage capacity of the three reservoirs is 40 million cubic metres.

5 — General view of the dam across the Angitola. The artificial lake so formed holds 21 million cubic metres of water, utilized largely for irrigation in the Plain of S. Eufemia.

1

3

4

5

1 — Reservoir for collection of water drawn from the river Mucone, part of the 233-kilometre distribution system for the irrigation of 3,500 hectares of land situated on the right bank of the river Crati (Cosenza).

2 — Reafforestation at Spinella in the locality of S. Giovanni in Fiore (Cosenza), an example of the considerable effort required in this type of land-consolidation intervention in the Calabrian Apennines for the protection of villages and of farmland in the underlying areas. Reafforestation of some 134,000 hectares has been completed in Calabria.

3 — Molarotta (Cosenza) forestry nursery, covering an area of 60,000 square metres. During the past decade the many nurseries financed through special intervention have supplied more than 30 million young trees for reafforestation projects.

4 — This weir, 100 metres long and 4 metres high, located downstream of the Tarsia dam, was built to check soil-erosion by the river Crati. Works for an aggregate volume of approximately 1.78 million cubic metres have been completed for the control of torrent water-courses in Calabria, in addition to the 3.3 million cubic metres completed with funds provided by the special legislation for Calabria.

5 — The Tarsia dam on the river Crati (Cosenza) is 10 metres high and approximately 115 metres long. Together with the installations on the Coscile, it forms part of an extensive system which utilizes a total of 52 million cubic metres of water from various sources for the irrigation, through a 300-kilometre distribution network, of 6,500 hectares of land on both sides of the Crati.

3

4

5

1 — This chemicals plant in the Crotone Industrial Nucleus (Catanzaro) produces simple and compound fertilizers.

2 — A 300-metre quay built in the port of Crotone, where the outer breakwater has been extended by 370 metres. Dredging of the harbour has also enabled the berthing of medium-tonnage shipping.

3 — A section of the 483-hectare Crotone industrial estate, where many plants, mainly in the chemicals sector, have already been established. New industrial projects for an aggregate investment of US $ 240 million have been located in Calabria.

4 — The Vibo Valentia Marina (Catanzaro) cement plant also produces lime and hydraulic binders.

5 — Reggio Calabria port installations. The Cassa has financed lengthening of the west pier and construction of the heavy-sea breakwater.

3

4

5

1 — Rail freight-car construction plant at Reggio Calabria.

2 — This plant at Vibo Valentia (Catanzaro) produces aircraft fuel-tanks, industrial furnaces, air-refrigeration plant, condensers and vacuum ejectors.

3 — Facility at Rosarno (Reggio Calabria) for the marketing and processing of citrus fruit grown by the many farms in Calabria.

4 — Advanced equipment of a chemicals plant at Crotone (Catanzaro) which produces pig zinc, sulphuric acid, cadmium and copper sulphate.

5 — Textiles factory at Praia a Mare (Cosenza).

1

3

4

5

1 — Detail of the auditorium of a theatre discovered during excavations in the Plain of Sibari to uncover the ancient Greek city, recognized as one of the most flourishing colonies of the Magna Graecia. Financial intervention by the Cassa has enabled the planning of an 'organic archaeological programme which is being carried out with the employment of the latest techniques.

2 — A hall of the National Museum at Reggio Calabria, the rooms of which have been modernized and laid out to enable appropriate exhibition of the works of art collected by the Museum.

3 — A holiday village at Isola Capo Rizzuto, one of the most attractive localities on the Calabrian coast; accommodation facilities include 293 rooms with 543 beds. With the incentives provided by special intervention 148 new hotels, providing 14,500 beds, have been built in Calabria.

4 — The cable cage-lift between Camigliatello and Monte Curcio (Cosenza) forms part of the infrastructures created for development of tourism in the Sila mountains.

5 — A hotel sited in the woodland that surrounds the lake at Cecita (Cosenza), a tourist and winter-sports centre in the Sila mountains.

6 — The promenade at Soverato (Catanzaro), here seen at night, is one of the infastructures created at one of Calabria's most renowned seaside resorts.

4

5

6

1 — Entrance and some of the buildings of CIAPI (Inter-company Industrial Vocational Training Centre) at Crotone (Catanzaro). The Centre was completed in 1965 and trains 400 students each year for employment in the electrical engineering and chemicals industries.

2 — Practical instruction at an experimental farm of the Agricultural Training School at Taurianova (Reggio Calabria). The school was opened in 1965 and accommodates 50 young people each year for specialization in modern farm techniques and domestic economy.

3 — Interior of the workshops of another CIAPI, located at Catona (Reggio Calabria), created in 1965 for the training of skilled workers for the electrical engineering and chemicals industries.

4 — The nursery school at Rose (Cosenza), completed in 1969, accommodates 60 children. In Calabria 177 new nursery schools have been built.

5 — Exterior of Cosenza Provincial Hospital, opened in 1969. The 350-bed hospital has divisions specializing in medicine, neurology and gastroenterology and a radiology department.

6 — Entrance of the 300-bed Nicastro (Catanzaro) hospital, opened in 1968. In Calabria 9 hospitals have been built or enlarged, providing an additional 2,810 beds.

7 — The 160-bed hospital at Praia a Mare (Cosenza) is equipped with many specialized departments.

3

4

1

5

6

7

BASILICATA

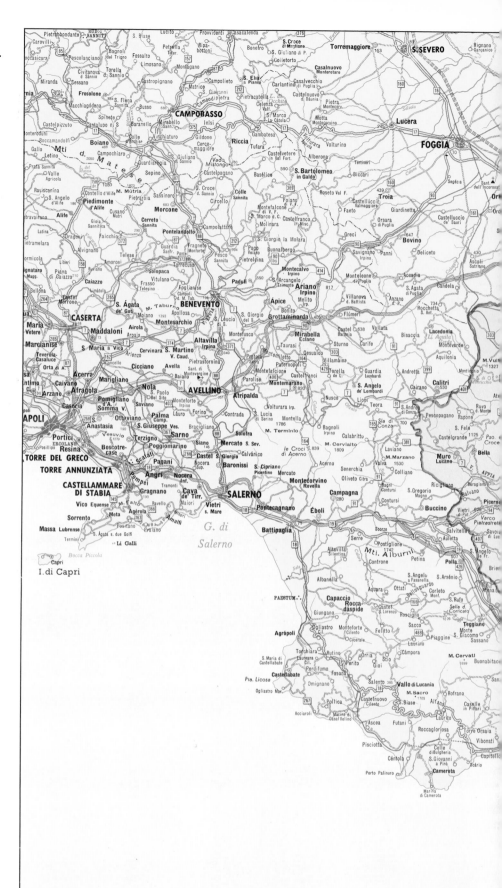

The Val d'Agri (Matera) divisor is one of the major distribution plants of the irrigation system fed from the Pertusillo reservoir which, through a 1,000-kilometre network of canals, adducts water at a flow-rate of 19,500 litres per second for the irrigation of 20,000 hectares of land in the Plain of Metaponto. In Basilicata as a whole a network more than 1,400 kilometres in length provides irrigation water for an area totalling 76,000 hectares.

1 — The 850-metre viaduct across the Tito torrent, along the technically most difficult section of the 30-kilometre Basentana highway, built by the Cassa to link Potenza with Romagnano. The entire artery provides a link between the Ionian coastal area of Lucania and the Autostrada del Sole.

2 — Panorama of the Mareatea and Mala-mogliera viaducts on the Fondovalle del Noce (Potenza) highway which runs from Praia a Mare, on the Tyrrhenian coast, to the Salerno-Reggio Calabria motorway. This 32-kilometre artery is another vital link in the chain of road communications in Basilicata.

3 — This reinforced-concrete viaduct, stretching for more than a kilometre across the Monticchio defile is the most important structure along the 77-kilometre road which follows the valley of the Agri (Potenza), linking the Plain of Metaponto with the Autostrada del Sole. The road passes through sections of geologically difficult terrain, necessitating the construction of approximately 400 metres of tunnels and 40 bridges and viaducts for an aggregate length of 4.2 kilometres.

4 — A reinforced-concrete arch bridge on the branch road between Lagonegro and the Fondovalle del Noce (Potenza) highway. The span of the 150-metre high bridge covers 140 metres of its total length of 350 metres.

5 — Entrance of the Prasti tunnel on the Fondovalle del Noce highway. Because of the extremely rugged terrain through which the road passes, it was necessary to build 30 bridges and viaducts, for an aggregate length of 3.5 kilometres, and 5 tunnels totalling over 650 metres in length.

6 — Road junction where the Basento valley opens out into the Plain of Metaponto, carrying traffic from the interior of Basilicata to the Ionian coast.

7 — A 510-metre viaduct-bridge over the river Basento on the 34-kilometre road between Ferrandina and Matera, which links the Valle del Basento Industrial Nucleus with the major highways leading to Apulia and Campania.

3

5

6

7

1 — The 650 cubic-metre reservoir at Metaponto (Matera) is fed by the Frida water-supply system which, through a 230-kilometre network with a flow-rate of 478 litres per second, serves a population totalling more than 200,000 in 24 municipalities of the Provinces of Potenza, Matera and Cosenza. Some 40 intake works, with an aggregate capacity of 1,510 litres per second, and 720 kilometres of pipeline have been constructed for extending domestic water-supply in Basilicata.

2 — The Policoro (Matera) reservoir, with a capacity of 350 cubic metres of water fed by the Frida system, supplies this important 8,000 population agricultural town in the Plain of Metaponto. In Basilicata a total of 46 reservoirs have been built, for an aggregate capacity of 50,000 cubic metres.

3 — The elegant span of the bridge carrying a steel pipeline across the Iesce canal. The water of this branch of the Apulian system is subsequently conveyed through a 20-kilometre reinforced-concrete pipeline to supply Matera with 230 litres per second.

4 — Panorama of tanks for the clarification of water drawn from the Basento and utilized by plants in the Matera Industrial Nucleus. The plant is capable of treating 2,000 litres per second, distributed through 10 kilometres of pipeline.

5 — Equipment of the Frida system pumping plant at Vena del Fico, for the supplementary and emergency water supply of coastal localities between Nova Siri and Metaponto.

3

4

5

1 — Pipeline-bridge of the Scanzano 38-kilometre feeder system in the Plain of Metaponto. The system provides 74 million cubic metres of water per year for the irrigation of 9,350 hectares of land in the coastal strip of the plain between Scanzano and Metaponto.

2 — The earth-fill Abate Alonia dam across the Rendina (Potenza), 26 metres high and 1,295 metres long, enables the storage of 22.8 million cubic metres of water. A series of such reservoirs provides for the irrigation of 26,000 hectares of land to the right and left of the river Ofanto.

3 — The concrete dam across the Pertusillo is 95 metres high and 312 metres long. Apart from supplying the Roccanova hydroelectric power station, the reservoir, which has a storage capacity of 155 million cubic metres, feeds the irrigation system which serves 21,000 hectares of land in the middle basin of the Agro and in the Plain of Metaponto. In addition, 450 cubic metres per second will be drawn to feed the Pertusillo system for the supply of localities in the Provinces of Taranto, Brindisi, Lecce and Matera.

4 — The load-bearing structures of the 2-metre diameter overhead pipe across the Cavone (Matera) torrent. The pipeline, which forms part of the Metaponto irrigation system, carries 5,500 litres of water per second from the Pertusillo reservoir to land in the area of S. Basilio.

5 — For irrigation of the Metaponto land-reclamation district this 700-metre crossing of the river Agri presented a challenging problem. The 1.5 metre diameter pipeline carries 2,400 litres of water per second to the highland areas of Policoro, Scanzano and S. Basilio.

6 — Panorama of some modern farms established in the Metaponto land-reclamation district. In Basilicata Cassa grants have assisted the construction of 16,300 new farmhouses, 635 km of inter-farm roads and 420 rural water-supply systems.

7 — The main square of Policoro (Matera), an important agricultural and business centre where a number of farm-produce processing plants have been established.

8 — Farming and infrastructures in the Valle dell'Agri (Matera) land-reclamation district in the Plain of Metaponto, comprising 40,000 hectares of land along the Ionian coast adjoining the borders of Apulia and Calabria. The availability of water, distributed through a 2,200-kilometre network, has generated a radical transformation of farming in this extensive area, aided by the construction of 1,000 kilometres of power lines and some 200 kilometres of roads.

4

5

6

7

8

1 — Reafforestation of 200 hectares of land upstream of the S. Giuligiano (Matera) dam to safeguard the reservoir which stores 107 million cubic metres of water for the irrigation of 12,000 hectares of land in the Valle del Bradano area, to the left of the river. In Basilicata some 18,000 hectares of land have been reafforested.

2 — An irrigation canal in the Metaponto land-reclamation district. Approximately 3,000 farms are served by the Metaponto Plain irrigation system.

3 — A rain irrigation installation in the Policoro area.

4 — Exterior of the Bernalda (Matera) olive-oil mill, which produces 400 quintals of oil per day.

5 — The earth-fill Ponte Fontanello dam is 45.5 metres high and 378 metres long. The reservoir stores 39 million cubic metres of water for the irrigation of the Pomarico land-reclamation district and for supply of the Ferrandina industrial area.

6 — The entrance of the Metaponto Horti-cultural and Fruit Consortium (Matera), created in 1965. The Consortium is formed by 18 farmers' co-operatives and provides for the processing and conservation of produce for placement on Italian and foreign markets.

7 — Detail of modern equipment installed at the Montalbano Jonico (Matera) milk station, capable of processing 90,000 quintals of milk per year.

3

4

5

6

7

1 — Industrial plants at Ferrandina, seen from the road linking the Basentana and Matera highways. In the Valle del Basento Industrial Nucleus, of which Ferrandina forms part, a number of major infrastructures have been completed, including the two afore-mentioned highways and the industrial water-supply system, equipped with a clarification plant. New industrial projects established in Basilicata to date have involved aggregate investment of approximately US $ 294.4 million.

2 — The sugar-refinery at Policoro (Matera) processes 1.5 million quintals of sugar beet annually.

3 — Detail of the chemicals plant at Pisticci Scalo (Matera).

4 — Assembly of electrical equipment manufactured in a plant at Potenza.

5 — Panorama of another industrial plant at Potenza for the production of railway and electrical equipment.

1

3

4

5

1 — The new railway siding for the chemicals plant at Pisticci Scalo (Matera).

2 — Interior of the workshops in the plant at Potenza which produces tractors and special trucks.

3 — View of a chemicals plant at Ferrandina (Matera).

4 — Buildings of the poultry-farm at Potenza.

3

4

1 — The remains of the Temple of Apollo Licio in the archaeological district of Metaponto (Matera). Built in the VI century B.C., the Temple was the first monument of the Magna Graecia with decorated pediments. Excavation work, made more difficult by the presence of ground-water, has enabled the discovery of further important architectural elements and also consolidation of the foundations of the Temple.

2 — A room of the museum built in the locality of Policoro for the appropriate collection of material discovered during excavation to uncover the ancient city of Heraclea.

3 — The Temple of Tavole Palatine seen from inside the Antiquarium which houses the important archaeological treasure discovered at Metaponto (Matera). Special intervention in the district is completed by an access road to the Temple and lay-out of the surrounding area.

4 — Panorama of the beach at Maratea (Potenza). Provision of incentives for hotel development in Basilicata has resulted in an increase of more than 2,100 in the number of beds available.

5 — Woodland surrounding the Monticchio Lakes (Potenza), another Lucanian locality capable of tourist development.

1 — The new 180-bed hospital at Policoro (Matera) was opened in 1970. Special intervention in Basilicata has enabled the provision of a further 1,750 hospital beds.

2 — Experimental poultry-breeding at the Viggiano (Potenza) Agricultural School, for the specialization of young people in dairy-farming and animal husbandry.

3 — Sport facilities and some of the buildings of Potenza Vocational Training Institute, which prepares 170 workers each year for employment in the electrical engineering industry.

4 — Practical instruction of students in the workshops of the Potenza Industrial Vocational Training Institute.

5 — Interior of a laboratory at the Viggiano Agricultural School, where young people are instructed in modern dairy techniques.

3

4

5

APULIA

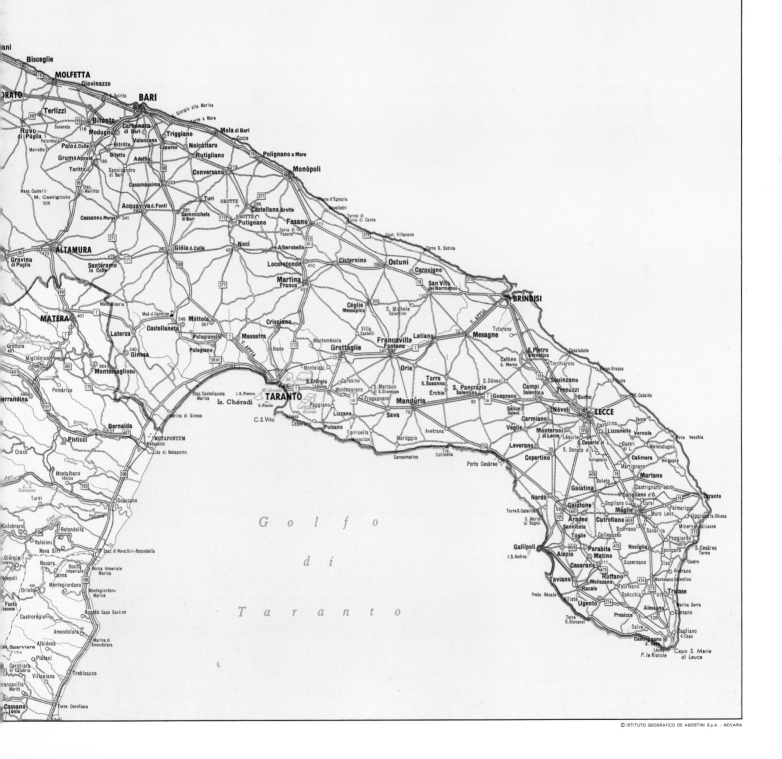

MARE ADRIATICO

Bisceglie
MOLFETTA
Giovinazzo
ORATO
BARI
Terlizzi
S. Spirito
Bitonto
S. Giorgio alla Marina
Ruvo
di Puglia
Sovereto
98
116
Modugno
Carbonara
di Bari
Triggiano
Mola di Bari
Torre a Mare
Cozze
Palo d.Colle
Bitritto
Valenzano
Capurso
Noicáttaro
Grumo Appula
160
Bitetto
Adelfia
Rutigliano
Polignano a Mare
Toritto
Sannicandro
di Bari
100
Conversano
16
Monópoli
Mass. Castelli
M. Castiglolo
506
Staz.
di Mellitto
96
Casamássima
223
Torre d'Egnazia
Savelletri
Cassano d. Murge
341
Acquaviva d.Fonti
Turi
GROTTE
285
Castellana Grotte
Terme di
Torre di Canne
Sammichele
di Bari
172
GROTTE
Putignano
Selva di
Fasano
Fasano
111
271
Gióia d. Colle
172
Noci
Alberobello
Cast. Villanova
ALTAMURA
473
475
171
360
420
Locorotondo
410
Cisternino
299
Ostuni
Torre S. Sabina
Gravina
di Puglia
96
Santéramo
in Colle
100
Carovigno
379
Martina
Franca
43
San Vito
dei Normanni
16
99
Céglie
Messápico
303
S. Michele
Salentino
110
BRINDISI
MATERA
401
Mad.d.Carmine
245
Móttola
387
Crispiano
Villa
Castelli
V. APPIA
Mesagne
Tuturano
Casalabate
Laterza
Castellaneta
Palagianello
7
Massafra
Statte
172
Montemésola
Grottáglie
133
Francavilla
Fontana
140
Latiano
72
S. Pietro
Vernotico
Ginosa
240
Palagiano
106 dir
V. APPIA
Monteiasi
Oria
Cellino
S. Marco
Torchiarolo
Borgo Grappa
Móntescaglioso
364
175
M. Pizzo
S. Giorgio
Iónico
Carosino
Monteparano
S. Marzano
di S.Giuseppe
Torre
S. Susanna
S. Dónaci
Squinzano
Trepuzzi
S. Cataldo
Pomárico
380
Staz. Castellaneta
Marina
I.S. Pietro
M. Grande
S. Paolo
Fragagnano
Mandúria
Érchie
S. Pancrázio
Salentino
62
Campi
Salentina
Surbo
errandina
167
Is. Chéradi
TARANTO
Faggiano
Lizzano
Sava
79
Guagnano
Nóvoli
LECCE
Bernalda
427
Marina di Ginosa
C.S.Vito
Tre
Grande
Leporano
Pulsano
Avetrana
Sálice
Salent.
Carmiano
Véglie
Monteroni
di Lecce
Lizzanello
Vernole
Pisticci
Metapontum
METAPONTUM
Torricella
Monacizzo
Marúggio
Campomarino
Leverano
Copertino
S. Cesário di L.
Castri
Calimera
Melendugno
Craco
Lido di Metaponto
Tre
Colimena
Porto Cesáreo
Galugnano
Martignano
Martano
Montalbano
Iónico
106
103
Nardó
Galátone
Sogliano
Soleto
Cavallino
101
Coriglíano d'O.
Otranto
Tursi
Torre S. Caterina
59
497
Máglie
Muro Lecce
16
L. d.
Gannano
Colobraro
104
Rotondella
Aradeo
Sannícola
Cutrofiano
Scorrano
S. Cesárea
Terme
Valsinni
Nova Siri
Staz. di Nova Siri-Rotondella
Gallípoli
459
Alézio
Parabita
476
Nociglia
Poggiardo
173
Rocca
Imperiale
I.S.Andrea
Matino
Supersano
Diso
Casarano
475
Andrano
Montegiordano
106
Ruffano
474
Montesano Salentino
Taviano
Melíssano
275
Tricase
Spécchia
Castro
d.Capo
Racale
Posto Rácale
Ugento
274
Alessano
Carsano
Torre
S. Giovanni
Presicce
120
Castrígnano
d. Capo
P. la Ristola
Capo S. Maria
di Leuca

Golfo
di
Taranto

© ISTITUTO GEOGRAFICO DE AGOSTINI S.p.A. - NOVARA

Port installations and industrial plants at Taranto, synthesizing effectively the process of economic and social progress under way in the Apulian city. The pier in the foreground, 3 metres high, more than half a kilometre long and 130 metres wide, stands in 16 metres of water, enabling berthing of the large-tonnage ships which serve the nearby Iron and Steel Centre. Some 33 plants have already been established in the 1,000-hectare Taranto Industrial Development Area, mainly in the iron and steel, metallurgical and engineering sectors.

1 — Port installations at Brindisi, where the considerable increase in the volume of shipping traffic, associated with the petrochemicals plants located in the nearby Industrial Development Area, has required major port development works. A 1½-kilometre underwater pipeline has been installed, enabling the unloading of crude oil at the rate of 2,000 cubic metres per hour, two new quays have been built, the harbour has been deepened to 10 metres and a buoy-mooring area created.

2 — Another view of Brindisi port, showing loading and unloading facilities.

3 — A berth for heavy shipping at Taranto. In recent years the port has been called on to play a fundamental role in the economy of the area, and the facilities have been continuously adapted to the growing requirements. Construction and expansion of piers, jetties and quays has provided an additional 2 kilometres of berthing space and a new 1,200-metre breakwater has been built. The harbour has been deepened to 16 metres between the Iron and Steel Centre dock and the S. Cataldo dock to facilitate handling of ships of up to 80,000 tons. The port has been equipped with new mechanical equipment and self-propelled cranes for the handling of goods and iron-ore.

4 — A section of the port at Bari, the third major shipping centre serving the Apulian economic development pole. The new S. Vito pier, 300 metres long and 50 metres wide, is one of the many facilities created at Bari port in recent years.

5 — The industrial quay at Taranto, equipped for the contemporary loading and unloading of four large-tonnage ships.

3

4

5

1 — The attractive 42-kilometre road between Mattinata and Pugnochiuso (Foggia) is an important artery of the network linking tourist centres in the Gargano district.

2 — This bridge over the river Ofanto (Foggia) is 6 metres high, 11 metres wide and approximately 300 metres long. It is one of the major structures on the Apulian section of the Fondovalle Ofanto highway, which provides 120 kilometres of easy driving from Avellino along the valley of the Irpinia and through the Vulture tourist district as far as Rocchetta S. Antonio, after which it provides access to the Autostrada del Sole at Candela.

3 — Another bridge over the Ofanto in the Province of Bari, 8 metres high, 9 metres wide and approximately 200 metres long, is situated on the road linking the Tavoletta land-reclamation district, on the left of the river, with National Highway 93.

4 — Electrification of the 299-kilometre Bari-Foggia-Pescara section, which has also been equipped with modern locomotives and electric railcars. Special intervention has contributed to improvement of traffic-handling facilities along this important line, enabling faster and more economical passenger and freight transportation.

5 — Entrance of the new Taranto locomotive depot, built by the Cassa in the framework of interventions for raising the traffic capacity of the Ionian line with the reconstruction of operating facilities and stations, track-relaying and modernization of superstructures along the 387 kilometres of line between Taranto and Reggio Calabria.

6 — Panorama of the highway linking Lecce with Brindisi and with the Adriatic motorway. This 34-kilometre dual-carriageway artery is capable of handling a heavy volume of traffic, providing fast direct communication between Lecce and Brindisi.

7 — View of the 10-kilometre road in the farming area of Torremaggiore (Foggia). This is one of the many land-reclamation roads built to complete the road system in the Apulian plainlands.

8 — This 5-kilometre road links the Casalvecchio and Casalnuovo land-reclamation districts with National Highway 160 leading to Lucera and Foggia. Some 2,500 kilometres of roads of this type have been built in Apulia.

4

5

6

7

8

1 — A close-up of the huge pipes of the Taranto reservoir, fed by the Apulian water-supply system. The reservoir has a storage capacity of 36,000 cubic metres of water, utilized for supply of residential and industrial development areas in the western part of the city.

2 — Plant of another large reservoir, which stores 38,000 cubic metres of water for supplying Bari. In Apulia 38 new reservoirs have been built, for an aggregate storage capacity of more than 80,000 cubic metres.

3-4 — Exterior and interior of the intake plant, fed by the Pollentina spring at Cassano Irpino, which provides an additional 2,500 litres per second to the water supplied by the Apulian system. To date 66 intake plants have been built in Apulia, providing an aggregate of 6,600 litres of water per second.

5 — Detail of the interior of the Modugno divisor, situated at the terminal of the new Andria-Bari branch of the Apulian water-supply system. The plant is capable of handling 2,000 litres of water per second, and is utilized to regulate allocation of the available flow-rate between the distribution network of the city's north-western residential and industrial areas and the reservoir seen in photograph 2. The new Apulian water-supply system comprises approximately 500 kilometres of pipeline.

3

4

5

1 — Detail of the Staina (Foggia) reinforced concrete siphon, 2.5 metres in diameter and approximately 10 kilometres long. The siphon forms part of the system fed by the Occhito reservoir for the irrigation of 138,000 hectares of land in the Apulian plains between the rivers Fortore and Cervaro.

2 — One of the principal reinforced-concrete canals of the system, fed by the water of the Rendina, for the irrigation of 4,500 hectares of land to the left of the river. More than 1,000 kilometres of canals have been built in Apulia, serving a total area of 170,000 hectares.

3-4 — Two views of the distribution and adduction plants fed by water drawn from the river Tara (Taranto) for the irrigation of 5,100 hectares of land in the areas of Massafra, Palagiano, Castellaneta and Ginosa.

5 — The earth-fill Occhito dam on the Fortore (Foggia) is 60 metres high and 432 metres long. The storage capacity of the reservoir is 292 million cubic metres of water, utilized for irrigation of the Apulian plainlands, domestic water supply of the city and Province of Foggia and for supply of the Manfredonia industrial estate. Two new dams have been built in Apulia, providing an additional water-storage capacity of 341 million cubic metres.

6 — Another large canal of the 440-kilometre irrigation system fed by the Tara.

7 — An overhead distribution canal in the left-bank area of the Rendina, part of a 30-kilometre irrigation system.

5

6

7

1 — Interior of the co-operative fruit
collection, conservation and packing station
at Trinitapoli (Foggia), with a handling
capacity of approximately 100,000 quintals
per year.

2 — Part of the co-operative wine-cellar at
Nardò (Lecce) which each year produces
53,000 hectolitres of wine grown in the
Salento area. More than 150 co-operative
plants have been built in Apulia
for the conservation and processing
of agricultural products.

3 — The Ponte S. Venere (Foggia) weir
draws 12,000 litres of water per second for
distribution to the Ofanto irrigation system,
which covers 40,000 hectares in Apulia and
Basilicata.

4 — Detail of the siphon which feeds the
canal linking the river Ofanto with the
Marana Capacciotti (Foggia). The steel
pipeline, 2½ metres in diameter and
3 kilometres long, supplies 12,000 litres
of water per second for the irrigation of land
to the left of the water course.

5 — The Montelupo siphon of the Ofanto
system, approximately 1 kilometre in length
forms part of the canal which links the river
and the Abate Alonia reservoir on the
Rendina and adducts the water utilized
partly for the Melfese district and partly to
supplement the availability of the artificial
lake.

6 — The oil mill at Terlizzi (Bari), built in
1965, processes 18,000 quintals of olives
annually and produces 3,600 hectolitres of
olive oil.

7 — The co-operative facility at Torremaggiore (Foggia), for the collection
and processing of 60,000 quintals of grapes,
produces approximately 50,000 hectolitres of
wine per year.

3

4

5

6

7

1 — Equipment of the plant at Taranto for the production of edible vegetable oils. To date, industrial projects promoted in Apulia have involved aggregate investment of more than US $ 1,920 million.

2 — View of the mineral oil refineries at Taranto.

3 — The reservoir which supplies the petrochemicals industry at Brindisi has a storage capacity of 750,000 cubic metres of water, which is distributed to the various plants through a complex pipeline network.

4 — Interior of a shop at the Taranto Iron and Steel Centre, which currently produces 6 million tons of steel per year.

5 — A pipe-production plant at Taranto.

3

4

5

1 — A view of the Brindisi petrochemicals complex.

2 — Exterior of the sugar-refinery at Rignano Garganico (Foggia), which has a processing capacity of 1,650,000 quintals of sugar beet and produces 200,000 quintals of sugar per year.

3 — Plant of a paper mill at Barletta (Bari).

4 — Equipment of the Applied Scientific Industrial Research Institute at Bari. The Institute is equipped with laboratories for metallographic, metallurgic, mechanical and water analyses and with an experimental system for the desalination of seawater.

5 — Assembly line of a plant at Bari which produces engines, gears and farm vehicles.

6 — Machinery for the production of pasta in a plant at Foggia.

7 — Another Apulian petrochemicals complex, located at Bari.

3

5

6

7

1 — Detail of the calcareous formations characteristic of the Grottoes of Castellana (Bari). Discovered in 1938 and opened up for a total distance of more than two kilometres, the grottoes represent the most important speleological complex in Italy after the loss of Postumia. Cassa intervention provided for improvement of access to the grottoes and for the equipment of lifts and electrically-powered vehicles for the transportation of tourists. In addition, new interior paths and passageways have been opened and a modern illumination system has been installed.

2 — A view of the Trulli at Alberobello (Bari). An organic series of special interventions has assured the preservation and valorization of the historical and characteristic buildings of the Apulian town, founded in the seventeenth century. In particular, intervention has provided for installation of the electricity supply system.

3 — The harmonious structures of Castel del Monte (Bari), typical of thirteenth-century architecture. Originally built for Federico II, the castle has been completely restored and consolidated. Similar interventions in Apulia refer to the preservation and valorization of 54 works of historical, archaeological and artistic importance.

4-5 — Two panoramas of the Apulian coast and of the hotels built at Torre d'Otranto (Lecce) and Pugnochiuso (Foggia), respectively, for the accommodation of the large numbers of Italian and foreign tourists attracted by the particular beauty of the two districts. The provision of incentives for the development of hotel projects in Apulia has resulted in an increase of approximately 13,000 in the availability of beds.

3

4

5

1 — Alberobello (Bari) nursery school, which accommodates 90 children, is one of the 47 such schools built in Apulia.

2 — Cassano Murge (Bari) nursery school, with accommodation for 120 children.

3 — Minervino Murge (Bari) Hospital, with 130 beds, was opened in 1968.

4 — The operating theatre at Galatina (Lecce) Hospital. Completed and enlarged by the Cassa in 1967, the hospital is provided with 400 beds.

5 — Another view of Galatina Hospital, from the entrance. Special intervention in Apulia has enabled an increase of more than 3,000 in the number of beds available.

6 — Grottaglie (Taranto) Hospital, completed in 1967, is equipped with 200 beds.

7 — The 200-bed hospital at Casarano (Lecce) is equipped with services which enable it to perform the function of a general area hospital.

3

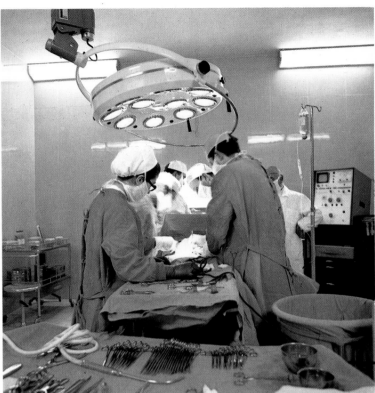

4

5

6

7

1 — Panaroma of CIAPI (Inter-company Industrial Vocational Training Centre) at Bari. Completed in 1965, the Centre trains 1,000 students each year for employment in the electronics, engineering and hot-working sectors.

2 — Entrance of the Research Centre for the Application of Advanced Technologies, Bari. In cooperation with FORMEZ (Training and Research Centre for Southern Italy) and Apulia University, each year the Centre trains 150 research-workers and technologists to advanced and intermediate levels.

3 — The garment-making department of the Barletta (Bari) Vocational Training Institute. With accommodation for 166 students each year, the Institute also promotes the training of radio and TV technicians and of engineers.

4 — The library of the Educational Services Centre at Taranto. A number of these Centres have been established to provide the public with documentation, also in sound and visual form, enabling understanding and study of the problems of Southern Italy.

5 — One of the many pieces of high-precision equipment installed in the Research Centre for the Application of Advanced Technologies, at Bari.

6 — A student working at the CIAPI Centre, Bari. Practical instruction completes the theoretical training of young people who have specialized in the various vocational training institutes in Southern Italy.

1

4

5

6

CAMPANIA

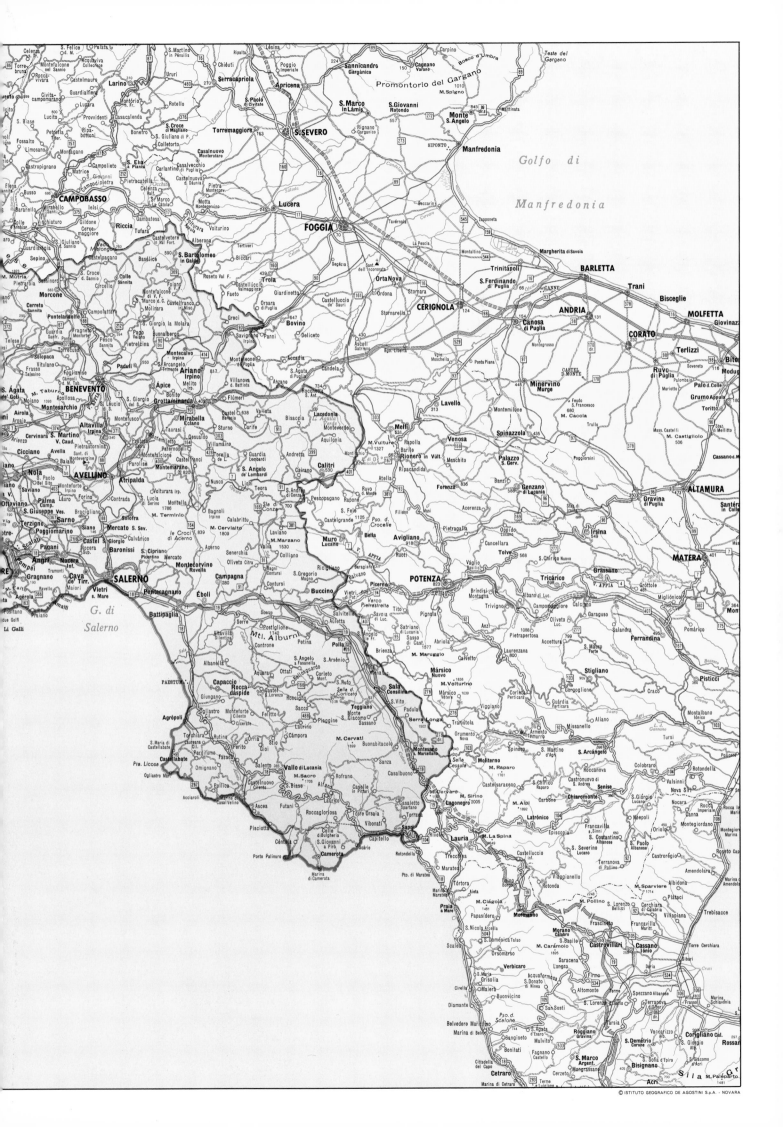

The 140-metre pipeline bridge between Procida and the islet of Vivara (Naples) is the intermediate section of a sub-marine pipeline approximately 13 kilometres long for the supply of water to the two islands and Ischia. It is one of the technically more difficult works of the vast Campano water-supply system which, by virtue of its length and of the originality of its planning and the boldness of the solutions adopted, is the most important water-supply project developed by the Cassa. The Campano system is capable, with an aggregate flow-rate of over 7,000 litres per second and a distribution network of almost 1,000 kilometres of pipeline, of meeting the domestic water requirements of 166 localities in the provinces of Naples, Caserta, Benevento and Avellino with a total population of approximately 3,800,000.

1

1 — The road between Palinuro and Marina di Camerota (Salerno) runs along approximately 10 kilometres of attractive Cilento coastline.

2 — The Anacapri-Punta Carena road on Capri passes through several of the island's most enchanting localities.

3 — The Sapri-Praia d'Ajeta section of the Battipaglia-Reggio Calabria railway line. Cassa intervention has not been limited to double-tracking and electrification of the line but has often involved complete modernization, with the rebuilding of major structures such as tunnels, bridges, viaducts and stations.

4 — Panorama of the Naples outer by-pass. The 28-kilometre artery, with two 7.5 metre carriageways divided by a 3-metre verge, links the roads radiating from Naples, thus eliminating the need for crossing the city centre.

5 — The winding road between Testaccio and Maronti on the island of Ischia (Naples) provides access to a long stretch of the Maronti beach in the municipality of Bairano.

6 — The Moiano-Monte Faito (Naples) road is another infrastructure for the development of tourism in Campania. The road, more than 6 kilometres long and 6 metres wide, rises easily from the Sorrento coast, passing through delightful countryside.

7 — The final stretch of the Pompei-Salerno motorway, here seen at night, presented one of the more technically challenging problems in the construction of the Cava dei Tirreni-Salerno section of the Autostrada del Sole.

5

6

7

1 — View of the installations built at Santa Maria la Foce (Caserta) for the intake of 900 litres per second of water for delivery to the Campano water-supply system. The photograph shows the 1,200 litres-per-second pumping station, the intake works and the 130-metre sloping tunnel.

2 — The source of the Torano (Caserta), together with that of the Maretto, provides 3,150 litres per second for the Campano water-supply system.

3 — Detail of the sloping tunnel built at Santa Maria la Foce (Caserta). Installations within the tunnel include a pipeline which raises water from the pumping station to a 6,000 cubic-metre underground reservoir and two descending pipelines for feeding the northern and southern branches of the Vesuvius section of the Campano water-supply system.

4 — The S. Rocco reservoir on the periphery of Naples has a capacity of 80,000 cubic metres. The reservoir collects the water adducted by the San Clemente-San Rocco-Santo Stefano pipeline of the Campano system and distributes it to the Naples district and to the Giugliano area as far as Licola.

5 — The purification plant at S. Giovanni a Teduccio, for the treatment of 1,500 litres per second of domestic refuse water from the eastern district of Naples. The Naples main-drainage system includes more than 200 kilometres of new pipeline.

6 — The tunnel which links the sources of the Torano and Maretto (Caserta).

7 — The electric pumps installed in the Portici (Naples) station raise water at the rate of 250 litres per second to the higher districts of Portici, Resina and Torre del Greco.

3

4

1

5

6

7

1 — Interior of the Maretto (Caserta) plant which feeds the Campano water-supply system. A total of 192 intake works have been built in Campania, providing an aggregate flow-rate of more than 19,300 litres of water per second.

2 — Pipeline bridge for carrying a pipe of the Campano water-supply system over the siphons of the Serino system: the 90-centi-metre diameter steel pipeline from S. Clemente di Caserta proceeds in the direction of Cercola-Naples. To date more than 3,100 kilometres of pipeline have been laid for water-supply in Campania.

3 — Detail of the pressure-vessel plant at S. Clemente (Caserta), where water is collected from the sources of the Biferno, Torano and Maretto for distribution through the pipeline leading to Naples and the western municipalities of Campania.

4 — This 227-metre pipeline bridge across the Volturno supports two 1.40-metre diameter pipes of the line from Monte Alifano-Limatola to Castelmorrone and S. Clemente di Caserta.

5 — Another crossing of the Volturno by a twin 1.40-metre diameter steel pipeline which adducts water from the Torano-Torre del Duca source and carries it towards the Bosco le Coste district and to the entrance of the Monte Garofalo tunnel.

6 — The underground arrival and departure duct of pipes in the Gasto reservoir, on the island of Capri, which has a capacity of 5,200 cubic metres. The Cassa has built a total of 533 reservoirs in Campania, providing a capacity of over 500,000 cubic metres.

7 — Exterior of the Villanova (Capri) pumping station, which raises water at the rate of 230 litres per second to the Gasto and Belvedere reservoirs.

3

4

5

6

7

1 — The earth-fill S. Pietro dam on the Osento (Avellino) is 50 metres high and 457 metres long. The reservoir stores 17.5 million cubic metres of water and forms part of an extensive irrigation system which serves approximately 27,000 hectares of land on both sides of the river Ofanto.

2 — A view of the weir across the Volturno (Caserta), part of the Sannio Alifano system for the irrigation of approximately 7,000 hectares of land in the Alifano plain, in the Presenzano and Vairano areas, the Plain of Lete and on the right bank of the Volturno.

3 — Crops in the Sannio Alifano (Caserta) agricultural development area. Irrigation has enabled the introduction of modern and rational farming, leading to an increase in the production of cereals, of lucerne for livestock breeding and, above all, of fruit and vegetables capable of industrial processing.

4 — Detail of the installations of the weir across the Volturno which draw 2,900 litres of water per second for irrigation of the Sannio Alifano land-reclamation district.

5 — Another of the seven take-off weirs built by the Cassa in Campania which provide an aggregate flow-rate of 27,000 litres per second for irrigation utilization.

6 — An irrigation canal in the Sannio Alifano (Caserta) land-reclamation district. The 430-kilometre system is fed by the water of the Volturno, Rio S. Bartolomeo, Lete and by the source of the Torano, providing an aggregate flow-rate of more than 8,000 litres per second.

1

3

4

5

6

1 — Equipment of the Mazzafarro (Caserta) station which pumps more than 1,000 litres of water per second from the river Volturno for the irrigation of 2,200 hectares of land in the area of Cancello Arnone.

2 — Detail of an intake work on the Garigliano (Caserta) and of the pumping station. The installations provide 6,000 litres of water per second for the irrigation of 7,200 hectares of land in the Cellole and Minturno land-reclamation district.

3 — Another example of specialized agriculture in the Sannio Alifano irrigation district. In Campania as a whole more than 136,000 hectares of land are irrigated through a distribution network totalling approximately 2,500 kilometres.

4 — The purification plants at Licola (Naples), which treat approximately 250 litres per second of domestic refuse water from Naples, for subsequent distribution to some 1,000 hectares of land in the Province of Naples.

5 — An irrigation raceway in the lower basin of the Volturno, which is covered by an approximately 365-kilometre distribution network.

6 — The Ponte Annibale (Caserta) weir is another of the intake works built on the Volturno. It enables the provision of 23,000 litres of water per second for feeding the irrigation system which serves 40,000 hectares of land in the Volturno Plain between Cancello Arnone, Capua, Grazzanise, Casal di Principe and Villa Literno.

4

5

6

1 — One of the nine co-operative plants financed in Campania for the processing and conservation of fruit and horticultural produce grown in the Region.

2 — A co-operative cellar belonging to a plant on the island of Ischia capable of processing 30,000 quintals of grapes per year.

3 — Interior of a greenhouse for the growing of vegetables. It is one of 16 such projects developed in Campania with special intervention financing, covering an aggregate area of approximately 15,000 hectares.

4 — Another wine-making plant, at Benevento, which produces 67,000 hectolitres of wine annually.

5 — The co-operative cattle-shed complex at Piedimonte d'Alife (Caserta) can house up to 5,000 head of cattle. In Campania approximately 16,000 cattle sheds, for housing over 90,000 head of cattle, have been built with special intervention grants.

6 — Panorama of the Fruit and Vegetable Consortium at Battipaglia (Salerno). The Consortium is composed of 19 farm co-operatives and is capable of processing 160,000 quintals of tomatoes per year and also engages in the production of oil and canned vegetables and fruit.

3

4

5

6

1 — A cement works at Naples. New industrial projects established in Campania have involved aggregate investment of US $ 2,784 million.

2 — View of the shipyard at Castellammare di Stabia (Naples).

3 — A petrochemicals complex at Naples.

4 — Interior of the plant at Pozzuoli (Naples) which produces typewriters and calculating machines.

5 — The Iron and Steel Centre at Bagnoli (Naples) has an annual productive capacity of 2½ million tons of steel.

6 — Detail of the installations of a plant at Pozzuoli-Arco Felice (Naples) which produces electric cand telephone cables.

7 — Buildings of the Alfa Sud plant at Pomigliano d'Arco (Naples), which will produce 300,000 motor vehicles annually. In the area of the plant site many infra-structures have already been completed or are being developed, including the service road to the motorway and national highway system, a rail link, the water reservoir and power-line connections.

4

5

6

7

1 — Assembly of a wagon in a plant at Caserta which produces railway rolling stock.

2 — Interior of the wool mill at Mercogliano (Avellino).

3 — The 40-hectare industrial estate at Cava dei Tirreni (Salerno), where to date 14 plants have been established, mainly for the production of ceramics and concrete products.

4 — A plant at Salerno which produces sanitary equipment and cast-iron radiators.

5 — The Garigliano nuclear power station, in the S. Venditto locality of the municipality of Sessa Aurunca (Caserta), generates 1 million kWh on average each year.

6 — Equipment of a modern plant for the manufacture of pharmaceutical products at Torre Annunziata (Naples).

7 — Aerial view of another pharmaceuticals plant, at Capua (Caserta).

5

6

7

1 — The mineral springs at Castellammare di Stabia (Naples) and the associated 205-bed hotel.

2 — Remains of the ancient city of Velia (Salerno), founded by Phocaen farmers in 540 B.C. A carefully planned excavation programme has enabled the uncovering of the Greek market-place of the city and the itinerary leading up to the acropolis.

3 — A hotel at Praiano on the Salerno coast. Incentives provided by special intervention have facilitated the construction of more than 400 new hotels, with a total of 28,000 beds, in Campania.

4 — The enchanting Sorrento landscape, seen from the terrace of a new 126-bed hotel.

5 — Interior of the Paestum Museum, where material discovered during the latest excavations is collected. The Museum was built with dressed stone, so as to harmonize architecturally with the lines and colour of the Paestum remains.

6 — A room of the Royal Palace at Capodimonte (Napoli), restored to its former splendour through patient and highly-skilled restoration work, which removed the scars of war. The Palace has also been appropriately arranged to accommodate one of Italy's most important museums by virtue of the value of the collection, which includes the porcelains and tapestries of the nineteenth-century Neapolitan school.

7 — The theatre of the Royal Palace at Caserta, where the Royal Chapel has been restored. To date intervention in Campania has referred to approximately 70 consolidation, excavation or restoration projects concerning archaeological and artistic treasure of particular importance.

3

4

1

5

6

7

1 — The modern buildings of the 250-bed General Hospital at Torre del Greco (Naples), opened in 1970.

2 — Benevento General Hospital, here seen at night, has been completed and enlarged and now has an availability of 230 beds.

3 — Panorama of the new 250-bed hospital at Nola. Special intervention has enabled an increase of 2,650 in the number of available hospital beds in Campania. It is planned to build a psychiatric hospital at Naples, with accommodation for 500 patients.

4 — Entrance of the S. Giorgio La Molara (Benevento) nursery school, which accommodates 90 children.

5 — A classroom of the Solofra (Avellino) nursery school, with accommodation for 90 children, one of the 236 such schools built in Campania.

6 — The frontispiece of Caserta General Hospital, which has also been completed and enlarged so as to accommodate 400 patients.

4

5

6

1 — The sports field at the S. Giorgio del Sannio (Benevento) Vocational Training Centre, which prepares 255 students each year for employment in the electrical engineering industry.

2 — Modern machinery used for practical instruction in a vocational training institute in Naples. Each year the institute specializes approximately 400 young people and more than 1,000 adults in electrical engineering, welding and carpentry and in the operation of machine tools.

3 — One of the refresher courses organized by FORMEZ (Southern Italy Training and Research Centre) for management and supervisory personnel of industrial firms, farms and of commercial and service enterprises, and for the officers of public bodies and consortia operating in Southern Italy.

4 — The canteen of CIAPI (Inter-company Industrial Training Centre) at Caserta seats 350 students and offers a typical example of the comfortable facilities provided at these Centres for the vocational training of new-entrants to industry.

5 — View of the Vocational Training Centre at Castellammare di Stabia (Naples) where more than 750 students are trained each year for the electrical engineering industry.

6 — Panorama of some of the buildings of the CIAPI Centre at Caserta. Completed in 1965, the Centre trains approximately 600 young people each year in electrical engineering, hot-working and in the operation of machine tools.

7 — Practical instruction in the chemistry laboratory of the Agricultural Training School at Cervinara (Avellino), where each year 80 young people are trained in modern farming and animal husbandry techniques.

8 — Interior of the Vocational Training Institute at Salerno, accommodating 450 students for specialization in electrical engineering and water-heating engineering.

4

5

6

7

8

MOLISE

The major structure on the re-routed section of Provincial Highway 28 (Campobasso) is the 920-metre tunnel through the Molise Apennines. The new 12-kilometre artery not only shortens the distance between the Casilina highway and Venafro but also eliminates the winding ascent of the Annunziata Lunga pass.

1 — The branch-road for Campobasso, seen from the viaduct. The new artery runs from the lower valley of the Tammaro to the road junction for Baranello, thus providing a fast-traffic link between Campobasso and the major highway leading to Benevento and Rome. The new road required the construction of many viaducts, for a total length of more than 1 kilometre, and of a 450-metre tunnel.

2 — The viaduct across the Ponte Liscione (Campobasso) reservoir is approximately 5 kilometres long and represents one of the most demanding structures required for completion of the Fondovalle del Biferno highway. Other bridges and viaducts, for an aggregate length of 12 kilometres, were built along the route of this important artery which enables communication, through the Tammaro valley, between the Tyrrhenian and Adriatic coasts.

3 — The 450-metre Monteverde tunnel on the Tammaro valley road, which runs for 48.5 kilometres through the Provinces of Campobasso and Benevento and, with the Fondovalle del Biferno highway, links the two Provincial administrative centres.

4 — The road between Larino (Campobasso) and the Fondovalle del Biferno highway is an example of intervention providing for the construction of minor roads to link promising agricultural centres with the Regional, and thereby the national, road system.

5 — Another section of the 81-kilometre Fondovalle del Biferno highway, which links the Plain of Boiano with Termoli and forms part of the major highway network built by the Cassa to eliminate isolation of the Molise Region.

1

3

4

5

1 — The 400 cubic-metre reservoir at Ferrazzano (Campobasso) is fed by the Molisano Destro water-supply system, which serves a total population of 271,000 in 76 municipalities with a flow-rate of 600 litres per second.

2 — A tunnel of the large Campobasso underground reservoir with a capacity of 9,000 cubic metres of water adducted at the rate of 130 litres per second from the Molisano Destro system, which supplies most of the urban centres of the Region through a 500-kilometre pipeline network.

3 — Another of the 213 reservoirs built in Molise, providing an aggregate capacity of 120,000 cubic metres of water for domestic utilization in the Region.

1 — Exterior of the S. Maria delle Macchie (Campobasso) station, which pumps 600 litres per second of water distributed by the Molisano Destro system. Some 62 intake works, with an aggregate flow-rate of 562 litres per second, have been built for the domestic water supply of localities in Molise.

2 — The 400 cubic-metre reservoir which provides the domestic water-supply of Morrone del Sannio (Campobasso) at the rate of 4 litres per second.

3 — Equipment of the S. Maria delle Macchie pumping station. Five electric pumps and two diesel pumps ensure the constant flow of water through the pipelines of the Molisano Destro distribution system.

4 — Interior of the S. Onofrio-Chiauci (Isernia) pumping station. Two electric pumps and a diesel-electric pump feed water at the rate of 204 litres per second to the other branch of the Molisano system, which supplies a total population of 160,000 in 46 municipalities of Molise situated in the area to the left of the Biferno. The entire Molise water-supply system comprises more than 1,000 kilometres of pipeline.

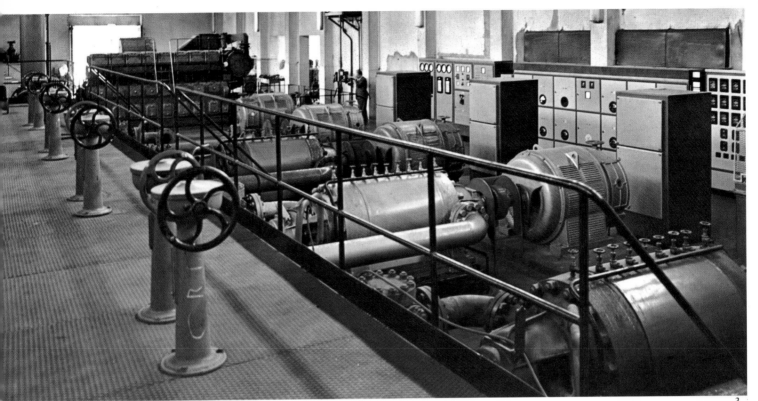

3

4

1 — Detail of the intake works on the river Volturno, in the locality of Venafro (Isernia), which enable utilization of part of the river water for the irrigation of 4,600 hectares of land in the Venafro, Pozzilli and Sesto Campano areas.

2 — Irrigation in the Plain of Termoli (Campobasso). This canal forms part of the 36-kilometre irrigation system fed by the river Biferno.

3 — The Ponte Liscione dam, under construction on the Biferno (Campobasso), will be 60 metres high and 497 metres long.

4 — Panorama of the Ponte Liscione dam. The reservoir will have a storage capacity of 173 million cubic metres of water for the irrigation of over 20,000 hectares in the lower valley of the river and for industrial and domestic utilizations. The reservoir will be crossed by the long 50-metre high viaduct of the Fondovalle del Biferno highway.

1

3

4

1 — Irrigation has enabled a radical transformation of agriculture in Molise. The photograph shows the gathering of strawberries, an example of the new and specialized crops now being grown in the Region.

2 — Rain-irrigation plant in an area situated between the Trigno and lower Biferno. More than 5,300 hectares of land are now irrigable in Molise.

3 — Rural electrification in the Larino (Campobasso) countryside. More than 2,270 kilometres of power lines of have been built with Cassa financing for the distribution of electricity in rural areas of Molise.

4 — The Marinella di Termoli (Campobasso) pumping plant. Three electric pumps located in the building at the end of the canal are capable of drawing water at the rate of 1,600 litres per second for the drainage of 300 hectares of land close to the sea. A further six similar plants have been built for the drainage of vast low-lying areas.

5 — An irrigation canal in the Plain of Venafro, where canalization extends for approximately 288 kilometres.

3

4

5

1 — A co-operative cheese factory at Isernia, capable of processing approximately 15,000 hectolitres of milk per year.

2 — The modern equipment of the milk and dairy-produce station at Isernia. A further six cheese factories have been built in Molise with Cassa grants.

3 — Panorama of the cement works at Guardiaregia (Campobasso). New industrial projects established in Molise to date have involved aggregate investment of US $ 38.4 million.

4 — View of the sugar-refinery at Termoli (Campobasso), which produces 163,000 quintals of sugar per year.

3

4

1 — General view of the archaeological site at Pietrabbondante (Isernia), one of the most important in the Sannio district. The first discoveries date back to 1846 and are of particular interest to experts since it would seem that the remains are, rather than of a city, of a religious centre of the ancient Sannian civilization of the II century B.C. The lay-out of the site was provided by special intervention.

2 — A hotel at Campitello (Isernia). Provision of incentives for hotel development in Molise has enabled an increase of 750 in the number of available beds.

3 — Panorama of Pescolanciano (Campobasso). Apart from its coastal resorts, Molise also provides for mountain tourism. Many infrastructures have been developed with special intervention in order to attract Italian and foreign tourists to the most picturesque localities and to valorize the immense natural assets of the Region.

4 — Detail of the theatre discovered in the archaeological area of Pietrabbondante. Of major interest are the elegant lines of the auditorium, a rare example of Hellenistic style, which also testifies to the high level of civilization reached by the Sannian people.

3

4

1 — Department for the specialization of young electricians at the Isernia Vocational Training Centre.

2 — The engineering workshops of INAPLI (National Vocational Training Institute for Italian Workers) at Campobasso are provided with the latest equipment for the training of young people in sectors of industry in which the demand for labour is greatest.

3 — Meal-time at one of the 99 nursery schools built with Cassa funds in various towns throughout Molise.

4 — Exterior of the Ferrazzano (Campobasso) nursery school, which accommodates 120 children. The new nursery schools built in Molise provide places for more than 9,000 children.

5 — Detail of the modern architectural design of the buildings which house INAPLI at Campobasso. To date financing has been provided for 8 centres or institutes in Molise, providing for the training of more than 410 students each year, predominantly for employment in industry.

3

4

2

I.N.A.P.L.I.
CENTRO
FORMAZIONE PROFESSIONALE

5

ABRUZZO
with Tronto Land-reclamation District

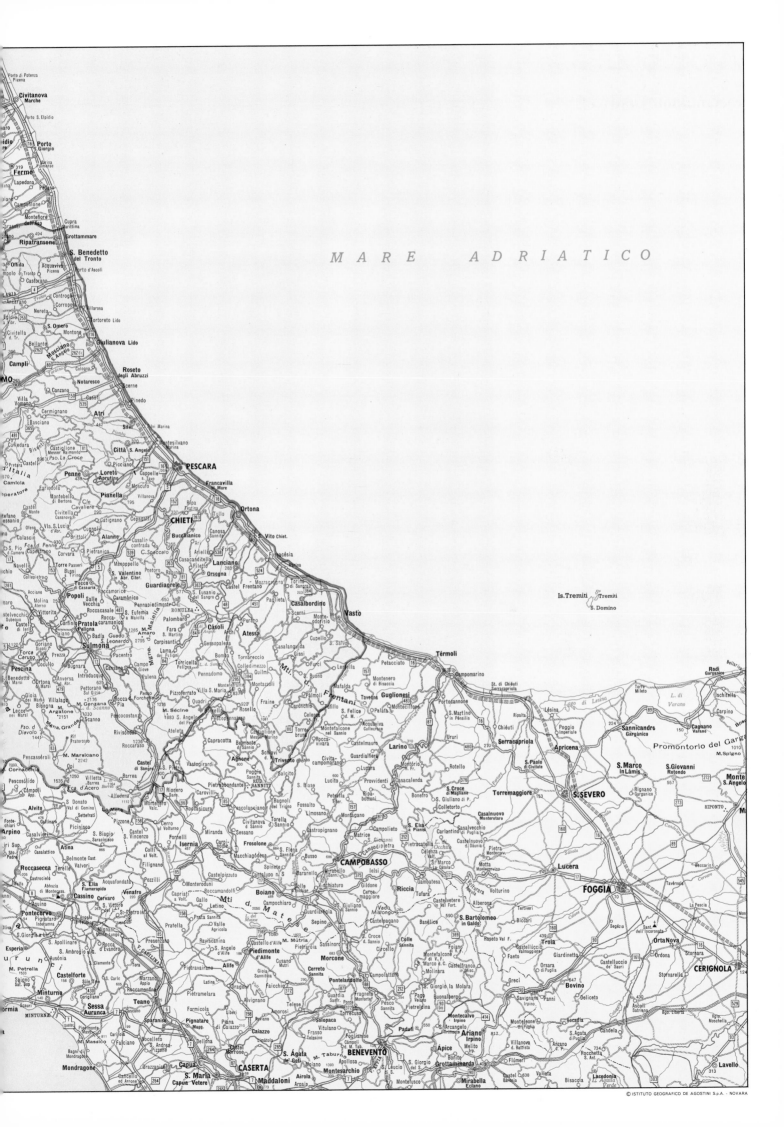

MARE ADRIATICO

Is. Tremiti · Tremiti
S. Domino

Promontorio del Gargano

© ISTITUTO GEOGRAFICO DE AGOSTINI S.p.A. · NOVARA

The arch bridge which carries the pipelines of the Verde water-supply system across the river Aventino. One of the most important in Abruzzo, the Verde system extends for more than 300 kilometres and, with a flow-rate of 460 litres per second, supplies Chieti and 36 municipalities in the Province of Chieti, with a total population of 163,000.

1 — The Chieti-Sulmona railway line has been entirely electrified and modernized.

2 — The bridge over the Vomano on the road built to link Cervaro and Aprati (Teramo) with National Highway 80. The span of the 46-metre high bridge extends for almost 70 metres of the total length of 108 metres.

3 — Entrance to the 477-metre Monte Castelluccio tunnel on the Fondovalle del Tirino highway, the construction of which has resolved a long-standing traffic problem for many agricultural districts, including Novelli and Bussi, in Abruzzo.

4 — The 70-metre Pietrasecca viaduct on the re-routed section of the Tiburtina highway leading to Carsoli (L'Aquila). The new 25-kilometre section improves driving conditions between Carsoli, Pietrasecca, Santa Maria and Tagliaccozzo and provides faster access to Lazio.

5 — Another view of the Fondovalle del Tirino highway, between Officina and Bussi (L'Aquila). For the completion of this road it was necessary to build many technically-challenging structures.

3

4

5

1 — Regulation chamber at the S. Sebastiano springs which feed the Ferriera water-supply system with a flow-rate of 500 litres per second. The 280-kilometre system was built to supply L'Aquila and 31 municipalities in the Province of L'Aquila, with a total population of over 70,000.

2 — A weir at Popoli (Pescara) on the Giardino water-supply system, which is capable of providing 1,350 litres per second. A 270-kilometre distribution system utilizes 800 litres per second for the supply of a total population of 320,000 in the Provinces of Chieti, Pescara and Teramo.

3 — Interior of the automatic pumping station of the system which supplies domestic water to L'Aquila and many other municipalities in the Province.

4 — The overhead pipeline crossing the Vomano at Roseto (Teramo) is part of the Vomano water-supply system which distributes 240 litres per second to Teramo and other nearby localities. The overhead steel pipeline is 220 metres long and 350 millimetres in diameter.

5 — A view of the off-take installations at Fara S. Martino (Chieti) which feed 460 litres per second to the Verde water-supply system.

3

4

5

1 — The 400 cubic-metre reservoir at S. Egidio (Teramo) is fed by the Ruzzo system which supplies water, at the rate of 380 litres per second through a 460-metre pipeline network, to a population totalling 174,000 in 33 localities of the Province of Teramo.

2 — The pumping station for supplying Chieti with water of the river Giardino at the rate of 120 litres per second.

3 — These reservoirs, which accumulate 6,000 cubic metres of water fed by the Ferriera system, supply the city of L'Aquila. In Abruzzo as a whole some 468 reservoirs have been built, for an aggregate capacity of 150,000 cubic metres of domestic water.

4 — Panorama of the reservoirs which store 18,000 cubic metres of water of the Giardino, for distribution to Pescara.

3

4

1 — A section of the large adduction pipeline which carries water from the Penne reservoir to the valley areas of the Tavo and the Fino (Pescara), for the irrigation of 1,300 hectares of land. The irrigation network in Abruzzo is currently 650 kilometres long and serves an aggregate area of 21,600 hectares.

2 — Canals in the Sangro-Aventino (Chieti) land reclamation district. Approximately 5,000 hectares of land are irrigated by a system which utilizes water from the rivers Sangro and Aventino.

3 — Pumps of the Ottomila land-drainage plant at Avezzano (L'Aquila), employed for the drainage of 5,000 hectares in the Fucino district. In Abruzzo a total of 28,200 hectares of low-lying and intermediate land are drained.

4 — Sluices of the irrigation scheme which which utilizes the water of the Pescara and feeds the distribution system for the irrigation of more than 3,500 hectares of land in the localities of Chieti, S. Giovanni Teatino and Pescara.

5 — Hydraulic works in Abruzzo have involved the construction of approximately 200 kilometres of levees and embankments and 200 kilometres of drainage canals for the protection of approximately 23,500 hectares of farm land.

6 — The earth-fill Penne dam on the river Tavo (Pescara) is 34 metres high and 438 metres long. The reservoir holds 9.2 million cubic metres of water for the irrigation of 4,000 hectares of land in the areas of Loreto Aprutino, Collecorvino, Moscufo, Città Sant'Angelo and Montesilvano.

3

4

5

6

1 — Detail of the weir across the river Tronto, the catchment area of which is the only territory of the Marche Region to fall within the area of intervention of the Cassa.

2 — An irrigation canal in the Tronto district.

3 — The Pescara farm-produce station, where modern equipment enables the handling of more than 150,000 quintals of fruit and vegetables per year.

4 — The factory of the Aprutino Consortium at Roseto degli Abruzzi (Teramo) is capable of producing 45,000 hectolitres of wine. In Abruzzo 104 wine-producing plants, for a total capacity of over 420,000 hectolitres, have been built, and a further 20 have been established in the Tronto basin, with an aggregate capacity of approximately 83,000 hectolitres.

5 — General view of the weir and sediment-ation and outlet tanks on the Tronto. The installation draws water from the river at the rate of 4 cubic metres per second for the irrigation of approximately 4,000 hectares of land in the areas of Martinsicuro, S. Benedetto del Tronto and Ascoli Piceno.

3

4

5

1 — A view of the 590-hectare industrial estate at S. Salvo, Vasto (Chieti) where a number of plants, mainly for glass-making, have been established. The provision of incentives for industrial development in Abruzzo has enabled aggregate investment of approximately US $ 428 million.

2 — A plant for the production of ceramic tiles at Teramo.

3 — Interior of a glass factory at Vasto.

4 — A fruit and vegetable conservation plant at Chieti.

5 — The paper-mill at Ascoli Piceno produces art and sheet-calendered paper.

1

3

4

5

1 — Detail of the sugar-refinery at Avezzano (L'Aquila).

2 — Fishing boats moored at S. Benedetto del Tronto. The Cassa has provided a considerable volume of financial grants for development of the fishing industry in Southern Italy. The benefits are evidenced also by the increase of the gross fishery product in the South, which has risen from US $ 44.8 million in 1957 to US $ 57.6 million currently (at constant prices).

3 — Interior of a table-china factory at Chieti.

4 — A wood-working factory at Avezzano.

5 — The machinery of a paper mill at Avezzano.

3

4

5

1 — The 1,705-metre chairlift which runs from Prati di Tivo to the peak of La Madonnina in the Province of Teramo.

2 — Panorama of Pescocostanzo (L'Aquila), another of the many tourist resorts in Abruzzo.

3 — A hotel in the Teramo mountains. The Abruzzo Apennines are renowned for their natural beauty, which attracts a constantly increasing number of tourists in all seasons of the year. Special intervention has enabled an increase of over 22,500 in the number of beds available in Abruzzo.

4 — The seaside resort of Giulianova (Teramo) has seen a considerable increase of tourism in recent years, aided by the construction of a number of hotels.

5 — The mighty ramparts of L'Aquila Castle, built as a fortress in the sixteenth century and restored with Cassa financing. Intervention in Abruzzo to date refers to 43 projects for the preservation of archaeological remains and restoration of monuments of particular historical interest.

3

4

5

1 — A wing of the newly-built, modernly-equipped, 380-bed hospital at Giulianova (Teramo). Construction and enlargement of hospitals in Abruzzo has enabled an increase of 2,500 in the number of available beds.

2 — The Educational Services Centre at Avezzano is provided with a reference library, a collection of newspapers and periodicals and sound-and-vision equipment.

3 — The nursery school at Villalfonsina (Chieti), accommodating 50 children, is one of the 149 new nursery schools built in Abruzzo.

4 — Interior of the Vocational Training Centre S. Antonio at Sulmona (L'Aquila), which prepares 312 students each year for employment in the electrical engineering industry.

5 — The Business Secretary Training School at L'Aquila.

6 — The Agricultural Training School at Avezzano (L'Aquila) instructs 70 young people each year in the latest techniques applied to agriculture.

7 — The experimental cow-sheds at the Avezzano Agricultural School.

8 — The CIAPI (Inter-company Industrial Vocational Training Centre) at Chieti was created in 1968 for the training of over 600 young people for employment in industry.

4

5

7

6

8

LAZIO
Frosinone, Latina and parts of Provinces of Rome and Rieti

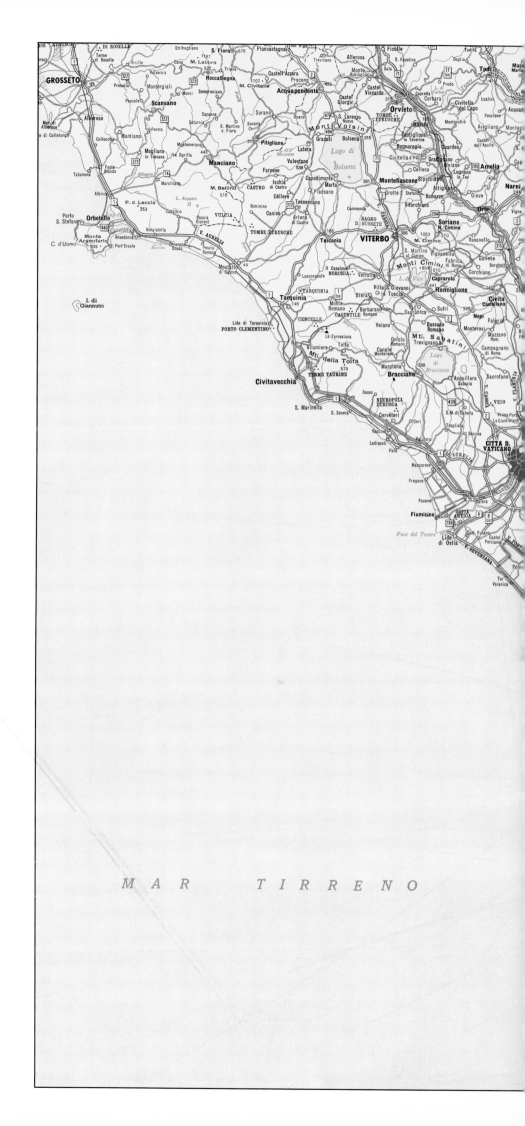

MAR TIRRENO

Panorama of the Terracina-Gaeta coastal highway, in the locality of Sperlonga. In the background is seen one of the four tunnels which, together with numerous bridges and viaducts, enable easy driving along this extremely difficult stretch of coast, especially the mountainous section between Sperlonga and Gaeta. Following the route of the old Roman road, the « Flacca », the highway harmonizes perfectly with a landscape of great tourist attraction, and at the same time provides a faster and safer alternative to the Appia National Highway. Together with the « Mediana », the highway represents a particularly important route for agricultural, industrial and tourist traffic between Latina and Formia and for longer distance traffic to Naples and Rome.

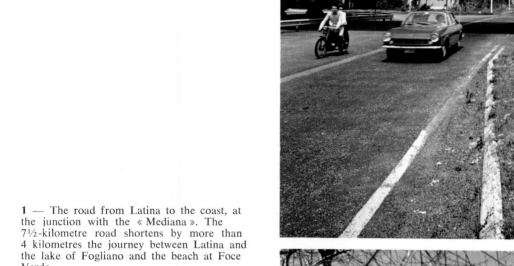

1 — The road from Latina to the coast, at the junction with the « Mediana ». The 7½-kilometre road shortens by more than 4 kilometres the journey between Latina and the lake of Fogliano and the beach at Foce Verde.

2 — The Giunture bridge across the river Liri (Frosinone) is approximately 100 metres long and more than 7 metres wide. It is one of the major structures on the 15-kilometre S. Giorgio a Liri-S. Apollinare road which links the two localities with Cassino and S. Angelo.

3 — Detail of the Anagni-Fiuggi (Frosinone) road which links the renowned Lazio spa with the Autostrada del Sole. The route of the road, more than 18 kilometres long and with a carriageway of 7½ metres, is through predominantly hilly terrain, but traffic moves rapidly thanks to the construction of several bridges and viaducts and a 672-metre tunnel on the section which passes through the foothills of the Ernici mountains.

4 — View of the « Mediana » road between Latina and Terracina, which joins the Pontina National Highway to the north and the Terracina-Gaeta road to the south. Approximately 45 kilometres long and more than 13 metres wide, the « Mediana » was built as an alternative to the Appia National Highway for taking the traffic of the land-reclamation districts through which it passes, of the S. Felice Circeo and Sabaudia tourist resorts and of the industrial plants established in the Latina area.

5 — This 126-metre viaduct over National Highway 207 is located on the 5 Miglia road between Padiglione and Lavinio, close to Aprilia (Latina).

6 — Some of the sharp bends on the 23-kilometre tourist road between Leonessa and Terminillo (Rieti), enabling rapid access to the ski-fields in the Vallonina area and the development of Campoforogna and Pian dei Valli as mountain resorts.

3

SAN VITO
S. FELICE C. LIDO

TERRACINA
NAPOLI

B.GO MONTENERO
S. FELICE C.

4

5

6

1 —- The surge-tank at Lavinio (Rome) regulates the flow-pressure of water provided by the Campodicarne system for distribution at the rate of over 100 litres per second to Lavinio, Lido dei Pini and Cincinnato, in the municipality of Anzio, with a total population of 45,000. Special intervention in Lazio has provided for the laying of 1,800 kilometres of pipeline and the construction of 381 reservoirs with an aggregate capacity of 86,000 cubic metres.

2 — The sluice gate and artificial lake of the Capodacqua (Latina) springs: the Capodacqua system supplies water at a rate of approximately 100 litres per second to the municipalities of Gaeta, Minturno, Castelforte and SS. Cosma and Damiano. To date the Cassa has built 83 intake works in southern Lazio for feeding the water-supply systems created with an aggregate flow-rate of 1,760 litres per second.

3 — Equipment of the Roccacerro station, capable of pumping 85 litres per second of water from the Verrecchie system.

4 — Exterior of the Roccacerro pumping station. The 300-kilometre pipeline network of the Verrecchie system, of which the station forms part, supplies water at the rate of 140 litres per second to 144 localities in the Provinces of Rieti, Rome and L'Aquila with a total population of more than 60,000.

2

3

4

1 — These pipelines leading from the Elena (Latina) pumping station convey water drawn from the rivers Sisto and Linea for distribution, at the rate of 3,000 litres per second, to 5,300 hectares of land in the Sabaudia, S. Felice Circeo, S. Vito and Montenero areas.

2 — Interior of the Elena pumping station, which supplies a 200-kilometre irrigation network.

3 — Water-course consolidation works along the river Amaseno, designed to enable the river to serve as the basic recipient of the head waters of all the catchment areas of the south-eastern areas of the Agro Pontino. Special intervention in Lazio for soil-protection has involved the construction of approximately 300 kilometres of levees and embankments, 157 kilometres of drainage canals and 4 land-drainage installations, whereby more than 78,000 hectares of land have been protected or drained.

4 — A raceway in the area of Fiumerapido in the Liri valley (Frosinone) between Cassino and S. Elia. The 85-kilometre distribution network supplies an area of 1,460 hectares.

5 — Rain-irrigation in the Pontina Plain, where Cassa intervention has included construction and consolidation of 125 kilometres of canals for the purposes of agricultural development.

6 — Reafforestation of approximately 700 hectares of land in the Rava-Mollarino (Frosinone) area, situated between S. Biagio Saracinisio, Picinisco and Vallerotonda.

7 — The Val Compra weir in the Conca di Sora (Frosinone) enables the diversion of 2,000 litres per second of water from the rivers Liri and Fibreno for the irrigation of 2,250 hectares of land in the areas of Castelliri, Sora and Lake Posta. To date more than 1,000 kilometres of canals have been constructed in southern Lazio for the irrigation of approximately 40,000 hectares of land.

3

5

6

7

1 — A modern co-operative wine-making plant at Aprilia (Latina), capable of processing 80,000 quintals of grapes per year, for the production of 65,000 hectolitres of wine. Special intervention has facilitated the establishment of 48 wine-making plants in southern Lazio.

2 — Bottling in a co-operative wine-making plant built in the Colli Albani (Rome) area and which produces 70,000 hectolitres of wine annually.

3 — Flowers being sorted at the Sabaudia Vegetable, Fruit and Flower Consortium (Latina), delivered from the specialized greenhouse and field growers in the intensive-agricultural Pontino area.

4-5 — The chemical-analysis laboratory and exterior of another co-operative wine-making plant at Aprilia (Latina) which processes 270,000 quintals of grapes annually for the production of 215,000 hectolitres of wine. The plant is capable of filling approximately 3,000 bottles per hour.

6 — Panorama of the co-operative wine-making plant at Colli Albani, which processes more than 80,000 quintals of grapes per year.

7 — The Sabaudia Consortium Station, to which are delivered annually approximately 25,000 quintals of vegetables, fruit and flowers for preparation, packing and despatch to Italian and foreign markets.

4

5

6

7

1 — Plants established in the Latina Industrial Development Area. To date credit facilities provided in southern Lazio have enabled aggregate industrial investment of over US $ 912 million.

2 — A detergents plant at Pomezia (Rome), seen at night.

3 — Interior of a plant at Aprilia (Latina), which produces canned meat and other food conserves.

4 — Panorama of a petrochemicals complex at Gaeta (Latina).

5 — Equipment of a plant at Pomezia which produces locomotive and asynchronous engines, high-voltage transformers and other electrical equipment.

6 — Manufacturing stage at an Aprilia glass factory.

1

3

4

5

6

1 — A hotel amid the snow at Terminillo (Rieti), one of Lazio's most renowned ski centres. Cassa intervention in the Province of Rieti has enabled an increase of more than 500 in the number of available hotel beds.

2 — The Temple of Giove Anxur on Monte S. Angelo at Terracina (Latina) dominates a panorama of exceptional beauty, from Circeo as far as the Gaeta headland. A wide road now provides easy access for visitors to the archaeological area.

3 — The Grotto of Tiberius (Latina), of which the interior is seen here, was discovered at Sperlonga during work for the construction of the Terracina-Gaeta highway. Used in ancient times as a swimming pool, it contained precious statues and other architectural treasure. A carefully-planned excavation programme carried out in the area enabled uncovering of the remains of the Imperial Villa and numerous archaeological discoveries, which are to be collected in a specially built museum.

4 — The central nave of the Abbey at Fossanova (Latina). Dating back to the ninth century, the Abbey represents the earliest example of Gothic-Cistercian architecture in Italy. Some extremely careful restoration work was necessary for consolidation of the load-bearing structures. Intervention in Lazio to date refers to some 30 consolidation, excavation and restoration projects of particular historical or artistic importance.

5 — Panorama of the coastline at S. Felice Circeo (Latina). Special intervention grants provided by the Cassa have facilitated the construction of new hotels in southern Lazio providing an additional 10,000 beds.

3

4

5

1 — The nursery school at Maenza (Latina) accommodates 110 children.

2 — One of the classrooms at the Maenza nursery school. To date 32 nursery schools have been built in southern Lazio.

3 — A wing of Formia Hospital (Latina), which was opened in 1967 after being completed and enlarged to provide 390 beds. Among the hospital's modern facilities in an automated analysis laboratory.

4 — The buildings of the new 460-bed hospital at Rieti. The availability of hospital beds in the southern Provinces of Lazio and in the area of Rieti has been increased by 1,500.

3

4

1 — Aerial view of the Agricultural Training Institute at Latina. The Institute, which occupies an area of 44 hectares in the centre of a fully-equipped demonstration farm, coordinates the activity of the agricultural schools at Frosinone, Cassino, Sora, Priverno, Formia and Itri. By virtue of the variety of specialization courses it is capable of providing, the Institute represents a typical pilot-centre. Approximately 500 young people are specialized each year at Latina in the latest farm-management techniques, whilst the Institute also trains teachers for agricultural schools in Southern Italy.

2 — The Vocational Training Institute at Anzio (Rome), where more than 250 young people are trained each year in engineering, welding and technical drawing.

3 — The Agricultural Vocational School at Priverno (Latina) trains 70 young farmers each year.

4 — The chemistry laboratory is one of the scientific facilities at the Latina Agricultural Institute, which is also provided with a reference library, auditorium, gymnasium, refectories and boarding accommodation for 160 students, and a teachers' training college with rooms and residential services for 100 students. The Institute is also equipped with a modern animal-husbandry centre.

5 — Practical instruction at the Anzio Vocational Training School.

6 — A wide range of techniques for the processing of cheese and other dairy products is applied practically in the dairy at the Latina Institute. A special co-operative, formed by the students, engages in direct selling on the market of dairy produce, fruit, vegetables and livestock production, thus providing useful commercial experience.

1

3

4

5

6

STATISTICAL
APPENDIX

Activity of Cassa per il Mezzogiorno
Economic Indexes relating to Southern Italy

Area of Cassa
per il Mezzogiorno Intervention

Ascoli P.
Teramo
Pescara
Rieti
Chieti
L'Aquila
ROMA
Is. Tremiti
Frosinone
Campobasso
Latina
Isernia
Foggia
Capraia Gorgona
Arcip. Toscano
Caserta
Benevento
Bari
I. d'Elba
Avellino
Isole
Ponziane
Napoli
Pianosa
Salerno
Potenza
Matera
Brindisi
Taranto
Lecce
Sassari
Nuoro
Cosenza
Cagliari
Catanzaro
Isole Lipari
Ustica
Isole
Egadi
Palermo
Messina
Trapani
Reggio C.
Enna
Caltanissetta
Catania
Agrigento
Isole
Pelagie
Siracusa
Pantelleria
Ragusa

----- Northern limits of Cassa intervention
——— Regional boundaries

STATISTICS RELATING TO CASSA PER IL MEZZOGIORNO

ROADS

	built kilometres	reconditioned kilometres
ordinary	3,476	16,240
highways	1,162	
tourist	1,016	972
land-reclamation	7,740	3,915
		million $
investment stimulated		856

TRANSPORTATION

railways	120	kilometres of line double-tracked
	911	kilometres of line electrified and modernized
	16	new diesel-electric locomotives
	70	new refrigerator cars
ferries	3	ships built for service between Sardinia and mainland
ports	21	docks enlarged
airports	3	airports under construction
	1	airport enlarged
investment stimulated	259	million dollars

WATER-SUPPLY SYSTEMS

1,400	intake works constructed for an aggregate flow-rate of
42,533	litres per second
14,914	kilometres of pipeline
2,746	reservoirs for an aggregate storage capacity of
1,604,182	cubic metres of water
2,225	localities provided with water-supply, for a total population of
8,494,881	inhabitants
1,021	million dollars of investment stimulated

AGRICULTURE

35	dams and **44** weirs constructed, providing a storage capacity of
2,025	million cubic metres of water for multi-purpose utilization
12,649	kilometres of irrigation canalization built
422	farm produce conservation and processing plants
2,453	million dollars of investment stimulated

LAND PROTECTION

195	villages consolidated or re-built elsewhere
966,193	hectares of land protected and drained
3,085	kilometres of levees and dykes
4,550	kilometres of drainage channels
15	million cubic metres of water-course control works
136,500	hectares of reafforestation
314	million dollars of investment stimulated

INDUSTRY

12,726	projects financed
4,942	million dollars of loans granted
527	million dollars of investment grants
8,680	million dollars of investment stimulated

TOURISM

166	million dollars for excavations, restoration works and tourist industry infrastructures
2,238	hotel projects financed, providing
71,786	rooms
235	million dollars of loans granted
368	million dollars of investment stimulated

SOCIAL INVESTMENT

agriculture	145	vocational training institutes and schools
industry	14	inter-company training centres
	299	training schools
services	66	hotel training schools
	68	hotel training courses
	104	other schools
trainees	90,000	qualified each year
school building	1,047	nursery schools
hospitals	66	buildings constructed or completed, providing
	20,795	beds
investment	382	million dollars

STATISTICS RELATING TO SOUTHERN ITALY

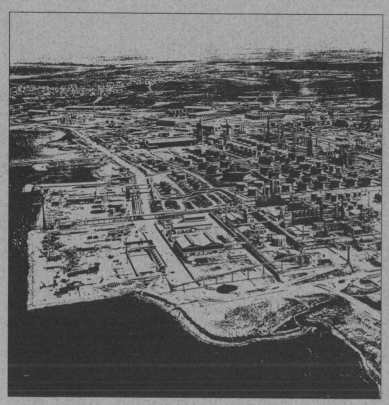

GROSS INVESTMENT

	1950	1969
	million $	million $
agriculture, forestry and fisheries	109.60	525.12
industry	174.72	1,121.12
transportation and communications	80.96	495.84
commerce, banking, insurance, professions and other services	68.00	506.56
housing	125.12	1,581.12
local government	112.48	489.44
inventory variations	101.76	65.92
total	772.64	4,785.12

ECONOMIC DEVELOPMENT

	1950	1969
	million $	million $
agricultural production	1,680	3,415
industrial production	1,014	3,941
	hectares	hectares
area under irrigation	275,000	700,000
	kilometres	kilometres
road system	42,897	94,578
	number	number
localities provided with water-supply	3,496	5,668
hotels	3,122	5,107

INCOME AND EMPLOYMENT

	1950	1969
	million $	million $
global income	5,635	13,584
	dollars	dollars
per-capita income	318	702
	number	number
employment in agriculture	3,679,000	1,966,000
employment in industry	1,228,000	1,830,000
employment in services sector	1,506,000	2,076,000

PRIVATE CONSUMPTION

	1950	1969
	million $	million $
food and beverages	1,729.76	6,182.08
tobacco	134.08	439.52
clothing and footwear	417.76	1,349.92
housing, fuel and electricity	298.88	1,729.12
furniture, furnishings, etc.	168.96	785.28
health and hygiene	154.56	1,149.44
transportation and communications	124.64	1,299.84
recreational and cultural goods and services	168.48	788.64
other goods and services	111.20	650.24

INDEX

Volume design
Enzo Gambino

Graphic art
Sauro Bertelli

Photographic services
Claudio Colagrande - S.P.S. - Rome

Other photographs
Giorgio Costa
Luciano Costa
Ferdinando Paladini
Mario Preite
Massimo Volpato
Italo Zannier

Printing
I.G.D.A. - Novara - 1971